Cultivating Wellness

· ·

Flourishing Physically, Mentally, and
Spiritually as a Woman of Color

· ·

By

Edna Laurent-Tellus, MSW, LICSW
Regina Pierre-Moise, Ph.D; MBA

Table of content

Dedication for Edna Laurent-Tellus:

This book is dedicated to my late mother, Julie Loreston Desvarieux. You were the wisest woman in my life, thank you for teaching me the meaning of unconditional LOVE.

To my husband, Enock Tellus, thank you for your unwavering love, support, and shared life lessons.

To my children and grandchildren, I am thankful for the joy you bring to my life and the opportunity you all provide by allowing me to continue my mother's legacy of unconditional love. I love you all to infinity.

Acknowledgment:

Infinite gratitude to my co-author, sister and friend, Dr. Regina Pierre-Moïse, for embarking on this journey with me. Your commitment to helping people build meaningful and harmonious relationships is truly a gift. I'm beyond grateful that you chose to share your passion with me by being a great contributor to this book and by your commitment to the vision of Awake IntuMind, Inc: To improve access to mental health services and to reduce the stigma that is preventing people from seeking mental health services, a vital component to their overall health. A big thank you to your loving husband, Dr. Frantz Moise, for his support and encouragement. Lastly, a special thank you to Lisa Nichols, my coach and sister in prosperity and possibility. Your words are still vibrating in my ears: "Write your book."

Dedication for Regina Pierre-Moise:

I would like to dedicate this book to my parents, Jonathas and Anne. You taught me that when life brings forth challenges that family keeps you grounded. I will forever be grateful for the guidance and support you have provided to me.

A special thank you to my husband, Frantz, for being such a pillar of strength in my life. I'd also like to express gratitude to my daughter, sister, brother, and spiritual sisters for their consistent presence in my life. I am truly honored to have such amazing people in my life.

Acknowledgment:

As the co-author of this book, I had the great pleasure of experiencing this journey with my confidante and good friend, Edna Laurent-Tellus. Edna, with our extensive history, I have been fortunate enough to witness your generosity, self-effacement, and overall zest for life. Please continue to be phenomenal and share your greatness with the world.

To conclude, we would like to thank all of our teachers, coaches, and clients who have imparted such fruitful knowledge upon us over the years. These exposures have served as the fuel necessary to ignite the motivation and confidence to write this book. May the healing begin and deepen!

Introduction:

Dear Sister,

I see you, carrying the weight of the world on your shoulders. I know you've grown accustomed to being overlooked, putting everyone else's needs before your own. Gracefully, you collect all of what life throws at you and place it in a bag. With the hope that its contents won't leak out, lest those closest to you see the reality of your pain. You may think that things won't get easier, but you'll get stronger. So you pick yourself up, and fight the good fight even though you may feel wounded in the process. Remember, you are a beacon of hope and yes, the world is blessed by your strength!

Our goal is to promote self-care, normalize the emotional challenges within, and encourage you to seek professional help, if deemed necessary, in order for you to flourish physically, mentally, and spiritually. Within these pages, you will find strategies to begin discovering the unconscious behaviors, thoughts, and emotions that prevent you from living your best life. We share our personal experiences as well as those of women we've been able to help along their journey of healing and prosperity. We are in this together!

Your sisters in the journey,
Edna & Regina

Chapter 1

Self-Care Isn't Selfish, It's Essential

S elf-care is critical for both our mental and physical well-being. You may have heard of the concept of self-care, but as a woman, you may feel that it is selfish to take care of yourself.

Whether you're a mother, a daughter, a wife, or perhaps all three, there is a possibility that you may think that it's your job to sacrifice the self to take care of others. While being a caregiver may be an important role for us as women, it is also critical that we employ self-care practices so that we can become and maintain the best versions of ourselves.

In the mental health field, self-care refers to purposeful engagement in any activity that promotes relaxation of the body and mind while aiding self-clarity. If you're a busy individual who is experiencing high levels of stress, take a moment and give your body and mind the opportunity to relax and breathe. Become involved in activities that help decompress and ultimately heal the body. Such activities can include, but are not limited to: getting enough sleep, following a proper diet, engaging in regular exercise activities, and finding time to do things that you enjoy (Baratta, 2018).

Research shows that self-care is effective and essential to maintaining good physical and mental health. Those who instill self-care practices on a consistent basis are less likely to experience high levels of stress, and report better overall health (Adkins-Jackson et al., 2019). The love and attention you give to others, you also need to give to yourself. Practice being light in body and mind by ensuring that you are attuned to your emotional, physical, and spiritual health.

Discovering Self through the love languages

As noted earlier, incorporating self-care appears to be an important factor in reducing stress among women of color. Two beneficial components of self-care involve improving self-awareness and fulfilling your spiritual needs (Baratta, 2018).

A simple way that women can possibly infuse self-care into their lives is by turning to the "five love languages" and applying them to their own needs. According to Dr. Gary Chapman, author of *The Five Love Languages*, each of us has a primary love language that demonstrates how we would like others to show us love. The love languages include: words of affirmation, acts of service, gifts, quality time, and physical touch. Our recommendation is to apply these love languages to yourself in self-care practices.

Let's begin by practicing self-care through words of affirmation, which entails speaking to yourself in a positive manner. For example, saying "I love myself. I am complete just the way I am." So often, women seek affirmation from their partner by asking questions such as, "Why don't you ever tell me I'm sexy?"

While it is encouraging for a partner to give us affirming compliments, as women we too need to be providing ourselves with positive affirmations as a part of our self-care routine. If you are struggling with self-esteem and self-worth issues and find it difficult to shower yourself with positive words of affirmation, no worries. Later in the book, you will learn how to train your brain to make this practice easier for you.

Beyond words of affirmation, acts of service towards yourself are equally important. How many times have you as a woman, found yourself taking care of others but neglecting your own personal needs? Women are often seen as nurturers who easily perform acts of service for other people, but we also need to be performing these acts for ourselves. These acts can include getting a massage, going outside and reading a book, or simply doing something that we identify as personally enjoyable. Again, we understand that it may be hard to break this habit of self-sacrifice because it is ingrained in our DNA. We will discuss the tools needed to break that habit later on in the book.

In terms of gifts, saying "yes" to yourself is priceless. While it may seem selfish, it is quite the opposite. This is because when you attend to yourself, you are able to care for others. Think of it this way: if today you get sick or die, then what will happen to those who rely on you? If you really love and care for them, then what better gift can you give to them other than being physically and mentally healthy? A gift to yourself can include, but not be limited to, getting a massage, indulging in the purchase of a new item, simply allowing yourself the time to go out for a walk, or participating in a yoga class at the gym.

As busy and stressed-filled women, it is also important that we partake in quality time spent with the self, doing things that we personally enjoy. This could include things that were once important to you prior to life becoming strained from work, parenting, or any other obligations you may face on a daily basis. Additionally, self-care should also include quiet time for yourself, as it grants you the opportunity to be still and nourish the body and mind. Such activities can include taking the time to get lost in a book, a few minutes of mindful meditation, or simply taking a nap.

Finally, physical touch is the last construct of the five love languages. Applying physical touch to the self may sound foreign, but it is equally critical for self-care. Unfortunately, this is often a neglected facet of self-care.

As women who are so busy taking care of others, we tend to rush through our basic self-care needs like taking a shower or simply applying lotion on our body. Engagement in these aforementioned tasks mindfully allows you to care for your body. Giving attention to your physical body in this way reminds you that you are valuable and it also connects the mind and body. This process can be especially healing since some women have the tendency to hold trauma in their bodies. Trauma physiologically fragments us, which can result in disharmony between the mind and body.

Have you ever experienced an anxious feeling in your body when your mind said that you should be okay? Taking care of the physical body in an attentive and loving way communicates to the mind that you are safe and can contribute to your overall joy and happiness.

To conclude, the mind-body connection is so powerful that simply placing a hand on an area where you feel tense can disperse positive energy and cause the body to relax. This physical touch allows the mind to acknowledge that you need to "slow down," brings conscious awareness to the strained body part, and releases the tension. Yes, let's release the strain and struggles within ourselves and apply love to those wounded areas. That is the one true way to really live a healthier and happier life journey.

How to love yourself without guilt

Even with a clear understanding of the five love languages and how you can apply them to yourself, you may still feel guilty about putting self-care into practice. If you struggle with this guilt, it may be helpful for you to consider that discovering a happier and healthier version of yourself makes you a better woman for those in your life.

For example, if you are happy and healthy, you will radiate joy and be a better supporter and caregiver for your family. For those of you who are married, it also has the potential to make you a stronger spouse. If you are not caring for yourself in a loving manner, then you won't have sufficient emotional and physical energy to care for others.

In addition, failure to love yourself can result in the development of destructive relationships. For example, if you aren't practicing self-care and do not love yourself, you can subconsciously attract unhealthy relationships. If you want others to love and respect you, then you must model such behaviors through your display of self-love. Understanding this fact allows you to stop accepting less than what you deserve and removes some of the guilt surrounding self-love. However, removing all of the guilt that can come with self-love can be challenging. As women, we have the tendency to neglect our own needs and self-care. Rather, we prioritize the needs of family or friends before caring for ourselves. We tell ourselves that we will rest after we take care of others. In order to love yourself without guilt, you must stop being secondary and act like the priority that you are, and view the self as a primary. So, taking care of number one is truly a prescriptive code for taking care of number two, three, and so on, in terms of how many people in our life we feel obligated to put first in our lives.

It may seem selfish to make yourself primary, but you can stop feeling guilty about self-love if you consider yourself to be a strong foundation for your family. If you love yourself, you will radiate an energy that makes others around you stronger. If you do not care for yourself, others may be harmed. As a matter of fact, if you have children, you are unintentionally causing harm by modeling to them that others are more important than themselves. So as adults, they will continue the legacy of "others first and me last," which will have destructive results in certain areas in their lives.

You must also consider yourself a model for those you care for. For example, if you want your children to respect you as a parent, then you must also respect yourself. When you model disrespect, you are indirectly teaching your children to disrespect you. This creates an issue called cognitive dissonance, in which children are told they must respect you, but they do not see you respecting yourself. More specifically, the behavior does not match what is being verbally shared. When you begin to love yourself, you are setting an example for those who are in your care and teaching them the value of respect. In this way, self-love should not make you feel guilty but rather should be the foundation upon which you teach your entire family about love and respect.

Finding a balance between collectivism and individualism

Have you ever felt that you must silence your own desires in order to please those around you? Perhaps it is helpful for you to understand that this feeling may be rooted in your own cultural values.

As human beings, our brain is wired to connect. It is that phenomenon that probably drove our human ancestors to bind together and to collaborate in a way that helped them survive in the wild and become the most dominant species on this planet. Recognizing the value of collectivism while understanding the importance of balancing this concept with individualism is essential in the acceptance of self-care, which is an integral part of building a happier and healthier life.

In a collectivist culture, we may lose our individual identities due to our focus being directed primarily on strengthening our family system. For example, I, Regina, was raised in the Haitian culture, where attention was placed on the community. I began to see myself through the lens of others while neglecting my own passions. I was a high-achieving woman who felt that I needed to attend medical school to become a physician in order to elevate the family name and help the collective group. I did this even though I didn't personally desire to become a medical doctor.

My family had this vision and due to my academic success thought that I should pursue a career in medicine. I struggled with whether I should become a physician solely to please my family. If I had chosen this direction, then I would have been adhering to the familial cultural values. However, I possibly would have become resentful, which would have ultimately hurt my family. Another option would be to explore additional career opportunities that intrigued me and explain my process for this decision. It had to be done in a manner that communicated its importance to me and the family system as a whole.

As you may have already guessed, I chose the latter. Rather than attending medical school to become a physician, I chose the route of psychology and became another kind of doctor, a psychologist. In the end, I had a conversation with my parents, during which I informed them that I was not interested in becoming a physician. I acknowledged their feelings. I then told them how honored I felt that they believed in my abilities and intelligence, but this simply was not what I wanted to do with my life.

By choosing to follow my own interests and becoming a psychologist, I was able to balance the individual and collective self. Instead of sacrificing my own individual aspirations, I communicated how important it was that members within the family seek and maintain their own happiness in order to avoid potential resentment towards the others.

To conclude, although I chose not to pursue a medical degree, my family was happy that I was still a doctor. I was fortunate enough to find a happy medium. How do you find this happy medium? In order to create such a balance, it is necessary to have a direct and healthy conversation with others, instead of engaging in fragmented conversations that are wrought with anger.

It may be helpful to think of this process as creating a sandwich. First, you begin with the bread, which is a positive statement. You will then move onto the meat of the conversation, which may include the critical concerns that could be viewed as negative. For instance, in the anecdote from the paragraph above, I did not want to become a physician but felt compelled to please my family. I began the conversation by saying to my parents, "You have done so much for me, and I am so grateful that you believe I should be a doctor." I then began to explain, "I don't know if I will do well in medical school, as it's not something I really want to do because I experience discomfort around excessive amounts of blood." I concluded the conversation (adding the last piece of the bread) by noting that focusing on being my best self only enhances my ability to be physically and emotionally available for the family.

In the long run, if you begin the conversation with a positive statement, you can avert defensiveness and possible arguments, as the brain tends to "shut down" when presented with negative information. Moreover, utilizing positive affirmations as a conversation starter helps stop the shutdown process from happening. It affords you the opportunity to have a conversation with your family where you are respecting the family's collective needs while also remaining true to yourself as an individual.

I, Edna, on the other hand, was born and raised in Haiti, and did not even know that I had that option to talk to my mother, who so desperately wanted me to become a medical doctor. The way I handled things back in the day (teenage years) was to rebel against or escape my collectivist household culture. I ended up getting married at age 19. My older brother told me on my wedding day that he knew that I got married because I wanted to leave the house (this is a conversation for another book).

I went on to enroll in college as a pre-medical student. During my second year in college, I fell in love with psychology and sociology. I considered myself an independent adult at that time and didn't have to ask my mother for permission to change my major. I went on to graduate school and had many successes as a clinician and senior executive in my chosen field. However, although my mother always supported me, she was very transparent that she was not happy with my choice. When I turned 50, my children made a video collage for me where they asked relatives and close friends to talk about me. My mom's comments were not surprising. After she said that she loved me and was proud of me, she added, "even though she is not a medical doctor." Classic Haitian mother!

The impact of the collective culture on my career was very unconscious to me until I was well in my fifties, when I decided to take my career to a new level. I noticed the cognitive dissonance. At a conscious level, I knew that I could achieve greater success based on my years of experience, but I found myself hesitant to take the actions needed to get me there. With the help of a therapist and a career coach, I was able to identify some behaviors that got me stuck.

For example, I had no interest in getting a doctoral degree because pursuing my passion didn't require it. However, I spent years of my life contemplating entering a doctorate program. Through my work in therapy and coaching, I realized that my actions were guided by my unconscious belief that having a doctorate degree would bring honor to my mom and my community. This belief was so ingrained in my subconscious that I was unable to be proud of my accomplishments over the years and felt that I had to keep learning. One of my daughters and a junior coach had to literally tell me to stop enrolling in classes so I could focus on developing my business. I never felt that I had true value to offer to the world just by being me. You see, I have been waiting for the expert to show up, only to realize that the expert was always inside of me. All because, I was unconciously unable to balance the needs of the collective with my own individual needs.

Strategies for nurturing yourself and your relationships

Understanding the importance of self-love and moving beyond the guilt and desire to please others are important for nurturing yourself and your relationships. There are additional strategies we can use as women to take care of ourselves and the people who are important to us.

One such strategy, which incorporates the idea of quality time for self, as well as the practice of giving ourselves the gift of saying "yes" to our own needs, is making time for physical exercise. Most of us are aware of the physical health benefits of exercise, but this practice nurtures us both mentally and spiritually as well. For example, research shows that women who increase their physical activity levels experience an improved perception of themselves, their physical health, and their attractiveness (Elavsky, 2010).

In addition to enabling you to nurture yourself, physical activity can improve your relationships with others. Exercise doesn't need to be complicated or intense in order to nurture you and your relationships. For instance, one study found that outdoor group walks taking place in farmland areas or green spaces reduced stress, improved negative moods, and enhanced mental well-being (Marselle et al., 2013).

Finding time to walk outside in green areas can benefit you psychologically while you are reaping the physical rewards that exercise offers. Also, sharing this activity with others will allow you to develop close bonds with them. Furthermore, by reducing stress and improving your own mental health, you are able to give more of yourself to others; thus, nurturing not only yourself but also your relationships with loved ones.

Another meaningful strategy that allows you to nurture yourself and your relationships is the practice of gratitude. We've all found ourselves getting caught up in the challenges of life, which can cause us to become negative and/or pessimistic. Taking time to acknowledge those things for which we are grateful for can have a profound impact on our physical, mental, and spiritual health, as well as on our relationships with others. For example, there was an interesting study in the *Journal of Health Psychology*. It was about a group of people that participated in a gratitude intervention, in which they were required to keep a journal that acknowledged the people and circumstances for which they were grateful for. By keeping this journal, their well-being improved. They experienced increased optimism, lowered blood pressure, and improved sleep, suggesting that gratitude enhances our spiritual, physical, and mental functioning (Jackowska et al., 2015).

The practice of gratitude can be extended to your relationships with others. Taking the time to express appreciation for your loved ones can eliminate resentment and nurture relationships.

Things to try today

As we've learned in this chapter, self-care is critical, and there are numerous ways to practice it. Knowing this information, you can make a commitment today to practice one self-care activity daily. This process doesn't have to be expensive, luxurious, or especially time-consuming. It can be as simple as taking a walk after dinner if that is what you enjoy, trying a new yoga class, or unwinding with a half hour of reading before bed each night. Whatever you choose, make a commitment to incorporate self-care on a daily basis. Imagine how different life would be if you allowed yourself to enjoy one thing just for you each day.

Another strategy to implement is taking the time to nurture at least one important relationship in your life. Whether this is reaching out to someone at work to tell them how grateful you are for what they do, or growing your relationship with your spouse by speaking up for your individual needs. Putting these strategies into practice will allow you to care for yourself and your relationships with others.

Reflections

Chapter 2

Establishing and Sustaining a Healthy Mental Attitude

Women of color may feel the need to be the saviors for their families and children, meanwhile they are suppressing feelings of being overwhelmed. Nevertheless, it is important for them to acknowledge these feelings, so they can equip their mind with the tools necessary to manifest positive mental attitudes, to aid in coping with trauma, tragedy, or stressors that arise throughout life. When tough times arise, women need to take time to reflect upon what the stressful situation is doing to the mind, body, and soul. It is also helpful for women to find someone they can speak with in order to process these situations. Unfortunately, women of color may feel guilty when they take time away from caring for others in order to cultivate a healthy mental attitude.

This guilt may be rooted in the common stereotype of the "strong black woman" who perseveres, even when it means sacrificing her own mental and physical well-being (Neal-Barnett, n.d.). If you are struggling with this mindset, remember that you cannot care for others if you are not well yourself.

In some situations, women may experience serious trauma and engage in self-blame. They may feel that God, the universe, or a higher power is punishing them, but they never take time to process the trauma. Sometimes, women are able to seek support and overcome the challenging situation, but other times, they may find it difficult to derive a healthy mental attitude. Some telltale signs that we may be experiencing an unhealthy mindset include, but are not limited to, mental health symptoms such as frequent feelings of irritation and/or frustration. When the mindset is not healthy, we may also feel that life is no longer satisfying and that we are simply going through the motions of life. Physically, we may feel tired and drained. Another symptom may be our abrupt reactivity to problems when they arise. During those moments, we may experience difficulty with connecting to our calm and healthy self. In those instances, it is critical that we ask ourselves and reflect on, "What is triggering this? Is it something I did? What has caused this change in me?"

An unhealthy mental attitude may also lead us to feeling that life has no true meaning and to question our purpose for existence. At this point, the mind is simply running on autopilot to allow for survival, but we are not accessing the brain's prefrontal cortex, which allows us to use the appropriate judgment to make wise decisions. In this state, if our thoughts are mostly negative, they have the potential to feel burdensome, causing us to feel weighed down as if we are being submerged underwater. How many of you feel the daily stressors in your life are drowning you? You are not alone. As a woman, I (Edna) have had the same feelings at times in my life. And I have many women who come to me describing these feelings. It is not uncommon for them to say: "I feel I am drowning"; "I'm barely keeping my head above water;" "I feel heavy". To illustrate how heavy and dangerous negative thoughts can be, I usually ask these women, what do you think makes humans drown in water? Some will be partially right by answering that it is because we drink a lot of water and were unable to breathe. It is true that our lungs are not made to breathe underwater; but what makes us go underwater in the first place? According to the law of physics, we are lighter than a mass of water. Such evidence would be that humans can float on water. Another is that once a person dies from drowning, their body usually floats back to the surface of the water. So, really what makes us go underwater in the first place is our fear of drowning. In that state of fear, all our energy goes into fighting the water which makes us heavy and unable to float. The same way that fear, which is at the root of every heavy/negative thoughts, can drown us in water, it can also drown us on earth.

How will I know the difference between a challenge I can tackle on my own and one that requires help?

Most of us have experienced some negativity from time to time, but when pessimistic thoughts prevail over rational ones, then it may be time to consider seeking professional assistance to address your concerns. As individuals, we know that we are managing a problem with healthy coping skills when we are still able to function normally in our daily lives without feeling mentally, physically, and emotionally depleted. Additionally, if you have balance and are enjoying your life, then it may not be necessary for you to seek services for your emotional and mental well-being.

On the other hand, if you find that you are not experiencing joy in the simple things like holding your child, and you find that daily tasks are a chore, you are likely "holding too much." A simplified example that comes to mind for me, Regina, was when my child wanted to show me something she was drawing. I was so consumed with the task of preparing dinner that I hesitated before attending to her. Perhaps you have also felt like this at times. You are so absorbed with getting through the tasks of a caregiver that you cannot take the time to stop and enjoy simple pleasures like playing with your child. If this is the case, then it is time to seek support to lessen the burden, restore your energy, and help find some balance. This support may be in the form of a therapist, a coach, or you might turn to people within your community or to a family member. Ultimately, the goal is to help you restore a sense of balance in yourself and in life.

There are some additional signals that can tell you that you need some extra support. For instance, having a stress-related migraine every day for several months is an indication of a problem that may require outside assistance. If your eating habits have become unhealthy or you rest but still feel tired, this can be an indication that you have become overwhelmed and overburdened. You may want to think of the stressors in your life like an onion; when they become too much, you may feel as if one setback after another has been piled onto you. To relieve the stress, it is recommended that you peel back the layers of the onion. This would be the opportune time to seek help.

If you are beginning to feel overwhelmed and are experiencing distress, it is highly recommended to seek help from a mental health professional, as you may not be fully aware of your symptoms. For example, if you are living with anxiety, your brain may never be able to rest, and you may find that it is affecting you negatively in multiple settings, such as at both home and work. You may find yourself in a panicked state or experiencing intrusive thoughts that prevent you from functioning in daily life. It is necessary for you to seek professional help, not only to address whatever mental health issues you may be living with but also to rule out physical health conditions, such as a thyroid condition.

When you see a mental health professional, he or she can use the *Diagnostic and Statistical Manual of Mental Disorders* to determine if your symptoms meet diagnostic criteria for a mental health challenge (American Psychiatric Association, 2013). You may not just be feeling stress; you could actually be struggling with a diagnosable mental health condition, which you will not know for certain until you seek treatment.

Dispelling some myths surrounding seeking treatment

Even if you're feeling overwhelmed with stress, you may be hesitant to seek treatment. Maybe you have been told that treatment doesn't work, or you've heard some negative myths about seeking help. Unfortunately, there are several misconceptions associated with seeking psychological treatment. One such misconception is that treatment is not necessary because we can rely solely on friends or family members for support. It is helpful to have supportive people in our lives, but sometimes our loved ones may minimize any problems we are experiencing. This is because they love us and want us to be okay, and seeing us hurt causes them some anxiety. Loved ones, therefore, may try to make problems smaller than they actually are because they want us to move on and be happy. This may be unhelpful and can deter women from seeking help.

Even celebrities, who seem to have every advantage, may struggle with reaching out for help. Activist and Actress, Jenifer Lewis has admitted that seeking help for bipolar disorder was one of the most challenging things she has done during her lifetime. *Empire* actress Taraji P. Henson, who has been open about her battle with depression, has encouraged women of color to seek therapy, as she feels the exercises that professionals can provide are more meaningful than simply talking to friends (Grant, 2019). These women of color serve as evidence that the myths surrounding mental health treatment simply are not true.

Another misconception about treatment that is especially applicable to women of color is that we should not seek support because we are strong women who should simply keep going instead of asking for help. There is a cultural expectation that we need to get up and go to work or "keep on moving." Lisa Nicole Carson, who starred in *Ally McBeal* and *Love Jones*, has been no stranger to this particular misconception. She has stated that by seeking treatment for bipolar disorder, she fought against the myth that African American women must be "pillars of strength" (Grant, 2019). As black women, we may think that we do not need treatment because we are still able to carry on and go to work. However, in reality, we are distracting ourselves from whatever mental or emotional turmoil we are experiencing. Eventually, this can lead to us becoming depleted.

The misconception that it is shameful to seek help is unfortunately common among Hispanic and Latina women of color as well. According to reports, very few people who identify as Latino seek the assistance of a mental health professional for a mental illness. In fact, only 11 percent contact a mental health professional, and only one in five seeks help from a healthcare provider (Arreola, 2015). Overall, there seems to be a reluctance to seek professional intervention among women of color.

Beyond the myth that women of color should stay strong and avoid treatment, there is yet another misconception that "mental illness" is not a real condition and that people who are struggling with psychological issues are being "weak" and need to "just get over it."

In reality, mental illnesses are, in fact, legitimate health conditions, which is why the *Diagnostic and Statistical Manual of Mental Disorders* details the symptoms of a multitude of mental health issues. These are not "made-up conditions" or signs of weakness. The conditions in this manual are health problems that warrant treatment. Adding to the evidence that mental illnesses are legitimate health conditions is the fact that these conditions affect the brain's physiology.

For example, research shows that among people with social anxiety disorder, there are higher levels of the neurotransmitter glutamine and lower levels of another neurotransmitter called GABA in the area of the brain called the thalamus (Pollack et al., 2008). This is relevant to mental health because glutamate is an excitatory chemical, meaning it causes brain cells to fire, whereas GABA is inhibitory, indicating that it prevents brain cells from firing (Queensland Brain Institute, 2017).

In simpler terms, this means women cannot fully separate their physical health from their mental health. The brain is an organ; therefore, it is part of the physical body, which means its physiology does affect psychological functioning. People who seek treatment are not weak; they are experiencing a legitimate health concern arising from what is happening physiologically in the brain. Historically, there have been stigmas surrounding mental health, where seeking treatment can be taboo. Among women of color who may experience discrimination in other arenas, such as in school or the workplace, seeking help for mental illness can add an additional layer of stigma. In actuality, receiving assistance for a mental health condition is no different than going to a doctor for treatment of diabetes or kidney disease. Furthermore, instead of being indicative of weakness, the act of seeking assistance for a mental illness is actually a sign of strength. It shows that a woman is striving for self-improvement and self-empowerment.

Even if you recognize that mental health conditions are legitimate, you may struggle with a final misconception—that treatment doesn't work. This may be a common misunderstanding, but the evidence does not support this belief. In fact, a review of 90 different studies found that a form of counseling called Cognitive Behavioral Therapy (CBT) is effective for treating depression, anxiety, and eating disorders (Cuijpers et al., 2016).

If you have come to the realization that it is time to seek outside intervention to achieve balance and improve your mental attitude, you can rest assured that treatment can work for you. Many women of color who enter treatment with us often question why they waited so long. They find the treatment to be so effective that it is not uncommon for us to hear them say, "everyone should be in therapy." They often recommend therapy to family members and friends.

What treatment options are available?

We know from research that treatment works, and fortunately, there are a variety of treatment options available to meet each woman's unique needs. For example, some women may need only a few sessions with a therapist to restore a healthier mental attitude, whereas others may require ongoing treatment to address their needs. In addition, some women may find that they do well with bi-weekly counseling sessions, whereas others may require intensive services and meet with a professional as often as twice or more per week. Lastly, treatment may occur on an outpatient basis for some women, whereas others who experience more severe challenges may require inpatient treatment. Whatever the circumstances, there are individualized treatment options available.

In terms of specific therapies, mental health treatment can involve psychopharmaceutical drugs and/or psychotherapy, which is the traditional form of "talk therapy" that most people think of when it comes to counseling (National Alliance on Mental Illness, 2020). Psychotherapy can occur in a variety of formats, such as through individual counseling, couple's counseling, or family counseling. Women may also attend support groups where they can connect with others who are experiencing similar challenges in life.

Finally, some women may find that they benefit from treatment that incorporates medications, such as prescription drugs that treat anxiety or depression. Many women benefit from a combination of therapy and medications. Research shows that a combination of the two is generally more effective than either therapy or medication on their own for treating depression and anxiety (Cuijpers, 2017).

Both medication and therapy can be helpful, and there are several specific types of therapy. One common form of talk therapy is CBT. This sort of treatment involves altering thought patterns that are unhelpful and contribute to an unhealthy mental attitude. The idea behind this type of therapy is that our thoughts control our feelings, which in turn control our behaviors. For example, if we think that we are not worthy, we may begin to feel depressed and, in turn, give up activities that we find to be enjoyable. CBT can be beneficial for women of color. A meta-analysis of 12 studies found that this form of therapy is highly effective for treating anxiety among people of color (Gregory, 2019).

While CBT is effective, it is not the only approach. Other forms of treatment include client-centered therapy, in which the therapist shows clients genuine care and concern to assist them with making changes, or existential therapy, which involves a therapist helping a client understand their perspective of the world while searching for meaning. Another common therapeutic approach is psychodynamic therapy, during which a therapist helps a client to investigate unconscious motivations to enable them to change behaviors and thoughts that are causing distress.

Some professionals practice holistic therapy, in which they integrate multiple approaches. Ultimately, women who seek treatment should find a provider who practices in a way that meets their needs (American Psychological Association, n.d.). Please note that there are numerous other therapeutic approaches, but we felt that it was necessary to mention and describe just a few in order to aid with providing a surface level of understanding.

The concept of mindfulness

In addition to specific therapeutic modalities, mindfulness interventions can be helpful for women of color. These interventions allow you as a woman to be "right here, right now" in the present moment. The focus is bringing the mind and body to the present. When you are not focused on the present, you are not truly living. Each moment is a gift, and if you are not being mindful (present), you are missing out on that gift.

Mindfulness can be helpful for women like us who may be so focused on multitasking that we never give ourselves the gift of being present. As mentioned earlier, as a mother, you may be busy cooking dinner while your child is trying to show you a drawing he or she has made. You are so focused on preparing the meal that you miss out on truly attending to your child and being present with them. If you focus on being mindful, your child will feel that energy and attention from you, and you will have the gift of creating a meaningful connection. You may be hesitant to be mindful, but the reality is that multitasking is not always beneficial, especially if you are constantly engaging in this sort of behavior. When you begin to feel overwhelmed, as if your attention is in multiple places at once, it may be time to practice mindfulness.

Practicing mindfulness requires you to eliminate distractions so that you can focus on the present. You can achieve this by turning off the television, taking a break from your phone, and stepping away from work or chores. If you are having trouble doing this, it may be helpful to ground yourself by naming three things you see in your environment.

For instance, you may make note of a blue chair, a red lamp, and a family portrait on the wall. This allows you to become attuned to the here and now. You may also benefit from practicing mindfulness meditation to help you focus on the present. You can seek out a practitioner who specializes in mindfulness meditation, take online mindfulness training courses, or utilize mindfulness videos to assist with this process.

Whatever method of mindfulness practice you use, you are likely to find that this act is beneficial to your mental health. A recent meta-analysis of 19 studies found that mindfulness interventions were effective for lowering stress levels among working adults (Virgili, 2015). If you find that you are feeling overwhelmed and you have become depleted, mindfulness is another strategy you can use to cultivate a healthy mental attitude. You can decide whether you want to practice it on your own or with the help of a professional. Ultimately, this is a coping strategy you can carry with you and turn to when you need some additional self-care.

What you can do now

If you are currently experiencing significant stress in your life, take the time to sit down today and assess whether this is something you can tackle on your own or is this a situation that requires professional intervention. Evaluate how the stress is affecting your life.
Are you able to find joy in everyday events? Do you still take time to practice self-care and spend time with your family? If this is the case,

you can probably address your stress by reaching out to a friend or carving out time for daily self-care.

On the other hand, if you are feeling so worn down that you collapse into bed at night, feel unrested in the morning, and cannot enjoy any given activity because you are so anxious about the next item on your to-do list, you would likely benefit from professional intervention. If you find yourself in this situation, reach out for help. Take the first step of calling and making an appointment, while reminding yourself that seeking self-improvement in this manner is a sign of strength.

In addition to assessing whether you are in need of professional assistance to manage stress, you can improve your mental attitude by making a commitment to practice mindfulness. Take just five minutes per day—perhaps first thing in the morning or during a lunch break at work—to engage in a mindfulness exercise. Close your eyes, take a few deep breaths, and focus on the present moment, allowing thoughts to come and go, but not spending any time ruminating on them.

Reflections

Chapter 3

My Life Partner

Relationships are another factor that can contribute to the mental health of women of color. Whether you are already in a committed relationship or are still seeking one, the topic of relationships is certainly relevant. Even if you think your love life is going well, imagine what would happen if you decided to make a commitment to improving it by utilizing psychological strategies.

For my Single Sisters: The process of inviting love in

For those who are single, there is often some pressure to find your person.

Achieving this involves determining what you need. This moves beyond superficial factors such as finding someone who is attractive or has a degree from Harvard. It requires you to find a person who allows you to be who you truly are.

To find the right person, you must first seek someone who is both your partner and your equal. You should not feel that you are less than or superior to your partner. To find a partner who is your equal, you must first invite love in, and this process begins with self-love. If you are not able to love yourself, then you will not be able to give and receive the love that you deserve. You will not be able to attract the right person either.

In the process of finding self-love and inviting in love from a significant other, women of color may face unique struggles related to stereotypes that people hold of black women. For example, hip-hop culture has created sexualized images of women of color, and these images often have a derogatory connotation. This has led to the development of the "Jezebel" or "Video Vixen" stereotype of women of color (Neal-Barnett, n.d.). We, as professional women, may have to overcome these stereotypes as we seek self-love and a relationship that is right for us.

I, Regina, had difficulty finding the right partner. This was due to others making me feel uncomfortable with my Ph.D. and having the designation of "Doctor" in front of my name.

While I was fortunate to ultimately end up with a phenomenal partner who also has a Ph.D., I thought I needed to minimize my professional accomplishments in order to be a suitable match for others. My distorted beliefs led me to feel that any significant other would not be supportive or possibly proud of a woman with a terminal degree, such as a Ph.D., especially if he did not have such a degree. My current partner pointed out to me, in a loving manner, that we were both equals during my process of overcoming this erroneous belief.

As women of color, we may have this misconception that women should be somewhat docile within their relationships. We must recognize our overall significance as women in order to invite healthy relationships into our lives. Allowing ourselves to be equal participants in our relationships is also a vital component in nourishing self-love. However, women of color may find this to be especially difficult due to the theory of intersectionality. The framework of intersectionality theory focuses on recognizing how the facets of a person's social and political identities can trigger discrimination. Women of color may feel that they are at a disadvantage in finding the right partner due to the intersection of being racial minorities and women. This in turn may shape their experiences more negatively when compared to those of Caucasian women (Anderson & Taylor, 2020). If women of color feel inadequate because of the intersecting influences of race and gender, they may experience shame and invite inappropriate partners into their lives. Once again, this is why self-love is so critical.

After you have taken the time to reflect and learn to love yourself, the next step towards finding the right person is by going out and meeting people. As you meet new people, you have to assess whether they are compatible with you. You may find that you're trying to head in one direction, while the people you're meeting are directing you elsewhere. During those moments, you may need to step back, reflect, and then redirect your attention to the self and assess whether or not you are truly practicing self-love.

For instance, if you continue to find yourself in emotionally and/ or physically abusive relationships, it is recommended that you take a step back, contemplate why you're in these situations, and make a commitment to love yourself. You may go through stages of trial and error before you are able to love yourself enough to attract someone who truly recognizes your value.

For my couples: Strengthening the bond

Even if you've already found the right person, the relationship will still test you from time to time. Fortunately, there are ways for you to strengthen your bond as a couple.

The first way to achieve this is to enhance your partnership. Ultimately, your person is not just your partner but also your friend. You must incorporate your partner into the areas of your life that help you grow so that they can see you flourish. For example, if physical wellness is important to you and helps you grow in self-love, you can strengthen your bond by sharing this passion with your partner.

Beyond developing a partnership, you must establish intimacy with your significant other. This can be challenging for some couples because it requires you to be vulnerable with each other. Ultimately, being vulnerable with your partner develops a lasting connection and trust, beyond what you can create with love alone. While love is necessary, it is not the only factor that makes up a successful relationship.

Aside from vulnerability, communication is key for strengthening the bond with your partner. You should never assume that your partner knows or grasps what is going on inside your head; you must communicate effectively. This process not only entails for you to be verbally expressive, which is a critical aspect of communication, but it will also require you to listen.

If you feel that your partner is not hearing you, ask them to share their perception of what you are trying to convey. After, try to verbalize your thoughts differently so they can have a better understanding of your perspective (Gottman, 2012). This process requires patience and understanding of the self and of your partner. Take the time to see things from your partner's lens and encourage them to do the same for you.

In addition, directing personal attention to your partner is also beneficial. If one partner is not loving the other in the way he or she needs, conflict can develop. If both of you are giving love the way that the other needs rather than how you want to be loved, the relationship will continue to strengthen, and conflict will be minimized. On the other hand, if you find that you are only giving minimum love and attention to your partner due to feeling a lack of reciprocity, then there is a potential that this could create a cycle where both of you do not feel truly cared for.

How two become one

Another way to strengthen the bond between couples is to look at how two became one. This is done by integrating different values, family backgrounds, and role expectations into the relationship.

To begin to understand this process, we can look at theories from both psychodynamic psychology and CBT. Psychodynamic theory assesses family history. It can be helpful to look at the way you were raised, including how your parents related to each other, because this information is reflective of your current relationships. A Psychodynamic approach can also affect the lens through which you view relationships and determine what kind of relationship you want. For instance, you may decide that you want the same relationship your parents had, or perhaps the relationship was not healthy, and you want a completely different relationship for yourself (Guntrip, 2018).

On the other hand, CBT comes into play when you think one way but behave in another. For example, you may decide that you do not want to behave the way your mother did in her relationship with your father, but in reality, you are behaving in that way. This creates a sort of cognitive dissonance in which your actions do not align with your thoughts or desires.

If couples counseling becomes necessary, you may find it helpful to explore and discover how you want the relationship to work. In therapy, you may come to understand that your childhood, which was the foundation that your life was laid on, affects the way you view others and behave in your relationships. Counseling may also involve both you and your partner taking a look at what was planted inside each of you growing up and the internal healing needed to healthily merge together.

It is also helpful to recognize that the seeds that were planted in us as children can affect us subconsciously. That is to say, we may be repeating behaviors we have learned during childhood without even recognizing this fact, and our partner may be doing the same.

Ideally, if we need to heal from what we learned during childhood, we will do this before becoming one with another person. However, if we find that there is additional healing necessary once we have already started a relationship, then we will need to discuss how we would like the relationship to look to our partner. This will likely involve addressing seeds that were planted during childhood and resolving any cognitive dissonance that may exist. Depending on how we were raised, each of us will bring different stereotypes, gender expectations, and perspectives to the relationship. This is why it is crucial to have a conversation about our differences and how we can integrate them into a stronger relationship.

Resolving conflict

If you run into conflict in your relationship, you must realize that working through disagreements requires both of you to work towards self-improvement and make the changes required to improve the relationship. Resolving conflict in relationships is not a one-person job. If you find yourself in conflict, then there is an assumption that both of you will do what is necessary to make the relationship work.

If you turn to couples counseling to address conflict, then both of you must be committed. You both should also prepare to discover things about yourself and identify areas for self-improvement.

Former First Lady Michelle Obama, in her 2020 documentary *Becoming*, revealed that she sought marriage counseling after the births of her children. She was getting aggravated with Former President Barack Obama's behaviors and wanted a therapist to "fix him." She said that she learned in therapy that she needed to love herself and engage in activities that bring her joy. So instead of being angry at Barack for going to the gym while she stayed home to take care of the girls, she realized that she also needed to create some time to go to the gym.

Family systems theory can help us understand this concept even better. This theory views families as units that operate together, instead of looking at each family member as someone who operates independently. This theory also states that families seek to maintain homeostasis, so if one member is struggling, then the others will adjust their behavior to compensate.

This can be seen in relationships with couples. For instance, if your partner has been stressed at work, you may begin asking for less from them, and eventually, you become resentful because they are not meeting your needs. It may be easy to blame them entirely for the conflict when, in actuality, you must also assess your own behavior since you played a role in the conflict by not expressing what you needed.

Dr. Murray Bowen's couples coaching, which utilizes concepts from family systems theory, applies nicely to this concept as well. It also integrates the idea of looking at roots and how they contribute to our behaviors in relationships. Bowen viewed families as "multigenerational emotional systems" (Baker, 2015). He theorizes that families not only act together as units, but they also pass down emotions and reactions from generation to generation. When resolving conflict, is it helpful to remember that you are bringing your own emotional reactions from your family to the table. You are also dealing with problems that you and your partner created together as well.

Additionally, when you and your partner are in the midst of a conflict, you must both be in the proper mindset in order to sit down and have a rational conversation. If you are so angry that you are not able to have a logical discussion, then you both will just be screaming back and forth. This is not helpful because resolving conflict requires you both to be talking and listening to one another. During times of intense anger, it can be easy to "fire" back and forth at each other without actually hearing what the other person is saying. It may sometimes be necessary for you to put a pause on the conversation and wait until your anger has subsided before you can work through the issue.

You can think of conflict resolution as a process that begins with acknowledging that there is a problem. You can then choose to address the problem, which means, "hashing it out now" or push pause on the conflict and hit the reset button later when you are ready to have the conversation. If things have gotten too "heated," it is not helpful to hash out the problem at that moment. You must have a healthy state of mind in order to address and resolve a conflict.

If you are too angry, your brain begins to run on "autopilot," meaning that you are not in the correct frame of mind to logically resolve a problem. In addition, when you are in this state of mind, your brain may be triggered by past traumas or problems. This in turn, will cause you to relive past conflict instead of having a conversation in the present. This process can be unconscious, and over time, it becomes normalized, creating a vicious cycle in which problems are never resolved.

Another consideration during times of conflict is that there is a difference between minor issues and larger problems, and we can often address minor issues without attacking and creating further conflict. For example, if your partner always leaves dishes in the sink and you find yourself having to clean up after them, instead of attacking them out of anger, you can calmly tell them, "I like when you clean and put your dishes away." This reframes the minor conflict. Instead of attacking your partner for what you feel they have failed to do, you are making them feel positively about doing what you'd like them to do instead. When you address minor problems in this fashion, you avoid becoming an annoyance to your partner and can help prevent major conflicts from developing.

Learning to forgive

Whether the conflict in your relationship is minor or serious, learning to forgive your partner is critical. You must recognize that forgiveness is not just for your partner; it is for you. When you are holding resentment toward them, you suffer as well.

Once you deal with the conflict, you must determine what you need in order to forgive. This process does not require you to "pick a side" or choose who is correct, but rather to choose the relationship. Forgiving and moving forward requires you as a couple to discuss what each of you needs from the other in order to achieve forgiveness. This conversation involves exploring what is necessary to allow each of you to begin loving each other again, and it also requires forgiveness from both parties.

Oftentimes, the solution for moving forward is that one member of the partnership wants a certain behavior to stop. Unfortunately, sometimes the other partner will state, "This is just how I am, and I'm not changing." If you arrive at this juncture, you must decide whether you can healthily forgive and move on, or whether your partner's failure to change will result in lasting resentment. You may decide that you cannot achieve forgiveness and that continuing the relationship will only result in ongoing unhappiness. In these cases, walking away may be best for both parties. Fortunately, in other cases, a couple may decide that they need to take time away to work on themselves so that they can forgive their partners. Ultimately, being able to forgive your partner requires that you are able to also forgive yourself. If you cannot forgive yourself for your own mistakes, then you will experience difficulty forgiving your partner. Healing from whatever past traumas or resentments will allow you to address conflict and maintain a strong, healthy relationship.

Tips for conversation

When you're engaged in a discussion aimed at resolving a conflict, you have an opportunity to strengthen your relationship. There are certain strategies that can make this discussion more effective. One strategy involves each partner having uninterrupted time to share their concerns and express their view of the conflict. During this time, the other partner should be prepared to listen without interrupting and respect their partner's speaking time. It is helpful if you listen for new information you didn't previously know, and if you think of something you want to say in response to your partner, write it down, instead of verbally interrupting. When you think your partner is finished speaking, ensure that they are, in fact, done, and then you may have your turn to speak uninterrupted (Beer & Stief, 1997). This process may seem foreign at first but with practice it can become an effective tool in maintaining good communication.

In addition to giving each other uninterrupted time to talk, it is helpful to listen for a "turning point" in the conversation, during which the discussion shifts toward a point of reconciliation. This may involve someone making an apology or making a kind statement. Once you reach this stage of resolving a conflict, it is time to begin the work of coming to an agreement that will allow you to forgive and release any feelings of resentment. After all, that is the goal of conflict resolution (Beer & Stief, 1997).

Putting it into practice

If you are in a committed relationship, take the time to think about a recent conflict you had. What was the source of the conflict? Was it rooted in values you learned from your family as a child? Take a moment to assess what you learned growing up and whether it aligns with how you'd like your relationship to look today. Identify areas where your beliefs, or how you'd like to behave, are in contradiction to how you are actually behaving in your relationship. Think about how you can make your beliefs and behaviors more congruent.

Next, think about how you can improve communication with your partner. Are you communicating in your partner's chosen style? Assess where there is room for improvement. Perhaps this will require you to refrain from reacting in a combative manner towards your partner when the discussion has become " too heated" to remain rational. As previously mentioned, it is impossible to have a sensible conversation when your mind is on autopilot. Once you identify what needs to change, put these changes into practice. You may even benefit from sitting down with your partner each week to assess how you are communicating and whether there are additional areas for improvement.

Perhaps your relationship difficulties are not with a committed partner, but instead involve difficulty finding a healthy, lasting relationship. If this is the case, now is the time to engage in some self-reflection. Assess your feelings about yourself and the way you present yourself to the world. Do you have any self-limiting beliefs? For instance, perhaps you think you don't have anything to offer to a partner, so you are attracting the wrong people. Imagine how your love life could improve if you focused on your strengths and began presenting those to the world.

Chapter 4

Shake Off the Shackles

All the principles from the previous chapters will be very difficult, and even impossible to master or practice if you don't learn how to "shake off the shackles." This involves tackling any unhelpful beliefs that are holding you back from becoming your best self. A common self limiting belief that we may have is that we are incapable of achieving certain dreams. These beliefs typically originate from negative childhood experiences, where the brain records certain information. For example, a parent may tell a child, "You have made a mistake!" The child may then internalize the belief, "I am not good enough." This programming stays in the subconscious mind and can influence the way we feel about ourselves as adults.

The unconscious mind operates rather automatically with limited effort. For instance, the habitual effects of waking up in the morning and brushing our teeth due to our engagement in this behavior on a daily basis. Therefore, it becomes a natural behavior. On the other hand, conscious behavior requires more effort. For instance, remembering an appointment or meeting requires conscious awareness.

Furthermore, subconscious (unconscious) programming from childhood trauma can create problems that begin to result in behaviors that we do not like. Such programming may make us believe that we must sacrifice our own desires to work full-time to provide for our families and care for our homes. This may result in us sacrificing self-care and becoming stuck and unfulfilled in life. In other words, the subconscious programming from our childhood melded with our cultural belief that sacrificing the self for the sake of the family can possibly limit us from reaching our full potential.

How to identify self-limiting beliefs

Tell us your strengths and we can show you your weaknesses. Very often, our self-limiting beliefs are masked as badges of honor when they are actually weaknesses. As individuals, we can identify self-limiting beliefs by understanding that certain characteristics we wear as badges of honor during periods of imbalance became our weaknesses. Others often exploit these qualities because of our desire to be top performers at home or at work.

For example, women of color may become "fixers" for their families, in which they are expected to provide financial support to family members or assist them with tasks like completing job or college applications. Over time, as these women give more and more of themselves to others, they have less leftover for themselves. This process eventually becomes draining and exhausting, so while being the family fixer may appear to be noble, it can actually be a weakness because it results in women being depleted and sometimes harboring resentments.

The desire to become a top performer can also lead to self-limiting beliefs, such as the thought that we as women must never say no. Over time, as we continue to say yes to any request that someone makes of us, we then become known as the person who is always available to help. Picture your own family. Is there a strong female figure who comes to mind who is always there to help? Perhaps it is your grandmother or an aunt, or maybe it is you. When you become the family fixer, this cycle causes you to become depleted and limits you from caring for yourself. You become out of balance, always caring for others but never taking the time to meet your own needs, which may lead to relationship and emotional problems.

Shaking off the shackles of negativity

While the desire to be a top performer and maintain badges of honor can be stifling, there are also other cases where women may be lacking confidence due to negative beliefs. In those cases, women may feel that they are not meeting their full potential because they are unable to shake off the shackles of negativity.

In our work with women, it is common to discover that women who have difficulties performing a simple task because of procrastination are perfectionists who are afraid to make any mistakes. An example of this may be that you are dissatisfied with your employer but find yourself putting off updating your resume and cover letter to apply for another job. Your reason for the delay may be that you want to ensure that your resume and cover letter are customized to fit perfectly to each job you apply for. By unpacking the self-limiting beliefs masked under a perfectionistic view, you may discover that it is your fear of rejection and people seeing you as being incompetent that are at the root of your behaviors.

As illustrated in the case above, the possible rejection from an employer can cause the brain to perceive the outcome as a threat. Hence, the brain will automatically create obstacles to stop you from taking action. We will expand on this concept in later chapters about the brain. Moving through life unconscious of these limiting beliefs may have dire consequences to your professional growth. You may find yourself not asking for help with a difficult assignment because you feel that you should know how to complete the task and would look incompetent if you asked questions. You may not apply for a promotion because you don't feel you have mastered all the duties associated with the position. Through counseling, a woman who is struggling with such a situation can learn to consciously overcome these limiting beliefs.

Once we recognize limiting beliefs, we can use strategies to begin correcting them. For instance, we may have the belief that we are not worthy of love. The first strategy to overcoming such a belief is to retrain the brain. We can accomplish this by repeating to ourselves, "I am worthy of love" first thing when waking up in the morning and again before falling to sleep at night. If you get stuck ruminating over a limiting belief during the day, you can repeat this phrase again in order to rewire and reprogram the brain. Over time, the statement "I am worthy of love" will become ingrained into your subconscious mind, thereby helping you to overcome the limiting belief.

A 2016 study in the *Journal of Experimental Social Psychology* found that self-affirmation helped people to recover from being socially ostracized. The process of retraining the subconscious is so important because, after about age seven, we need repetition in order to retrain the brain. Repeating positive statements can be especially helpful, as research has shown. So, if you have been feeling negatively and have developed self-limiting beliefs as a result, repeating positive statements can be beneficial. These statements are also helpful if you have a history of trauma or negative experiences that have normalized self-limiting beliefs for you.

According to the Healing Trauma Center, the brain lays down automatic pathways in response to trauma, so that a trauma-related response such as "emotional arousal" or "shutting down" becomes the norm. Have you ever found yourself in a situation where you felt paralyzed? It may be the freeze mode of the survival responses, which are commonly known as "fight or flight." The Polyvagal theory is a very important contributor to our understanding of how the brain responds to trauma or traumatic experiences in general. That theory helps us see the interconnection between our emotional state and our bodily or physical response. Often, we hear that women of color tend to experience psychosomatic distress, which refers to people feeling physically ill in response to being in stressful or difficult environments. For example, think of women who are in difficult marriages, which they cannot escape. You would not be surprised to hear that they frequently experience stomach issues, pain that is not associated to an injury or even uncontrollable bowel movement especially when they are near the source of their stress (e.g. that spouse).

Well, the Polyvagal theory helps us understand these women's physical discomforts by shedding light on the role of the Vagus nerve, which is the longest nerve in our body, that connects our brain to our heart, lung and digestive system (i.e., gut). The connection between the vagus nerve and the aforementioned parts of the body explain how we feel in stressful social situations. In most situations, when we feel that we are in danger or the situation is unsafe, the nerve lets our body know to either freeze (give up the fight) or fight back (fight for survival). How many of you can relate to someone who feels very sensitive to the stressors around them? How many of you go to work and feel like you have to watch out for yourself because you know that you do not feel protected there? For anyone who is interested in gaining a deeper understanding of this theory, Dr. Porges' polyvagal theory is a great starting point. His innovative work demonstrates that the freeze response is very common in victims of trauma. It usually manifests itself through "dissociation."

Fortunately, we can rewire the brain with self-affirming statements so that we can heal from trauma and choose a different response. This shakes off the shackles of negativity, removes us from a place of being stuck, and allows us to move forward and reach our full potential as women.

Tools to use

Now that you've learned about self-limiting beliefs and where they originate, take the time to identify one from your own life. Perhaps you believe that you are not a competent employee, or that your parenting skills are poor. Once you identify the belief, make a habit of practicing positive affirmations each day, morning and night, to overcome this belief. For instance, repeat to yourself, "I am a good mother" and watch as your beliefs about yourself and your parenting skills improve.

In addition, here are our top five positive affirmations that can rewire the brain and aid with healing:

I am worthy of love.
I am intelligent and capable.
I am valuable to my family.
I deserve to be treated with respect.
I make positive contributions to the lives of others.

Reflections

Chapter 5

Roots Produce Fruits

According to neuroscience the brain is not fully mature until adulthood. The prefrontal cortex, which is located behind our forehead and acts as the seat of our consciousness, is the last part of the brain to be fully developed.

In order to produce mental healing, it is critical to unearth and address childhood memories. This process operates according to the principle that "roots produce fruits." In more straightforward terms, our childhood histories, or our roots, create current thoughts and behaviors, which are fruits. To achieve healing, you must first identify these childhood roots so that you can correct anything negative that was planted into your brain as a child. A useful analogy for understanding this concept is that of a computer. Think of your childhood memories as being part of your subconscious. These memories are the software that allows the computer to function. Whatever memories are "put into" the computer from the beginning affect what "comes out," which are our thoughts, feelings, and behaviors. Much like a computer, if "garbage" is planted into the hardware, garbage is what will come out of it. If both negative and false information are planted in our minds during our childhood, this has the potential to replicate itself during our adulthood in the form of negative thoughts, feelings, and behaviors.

This process of creating our software is subconscious, and it begins early in life. In fact, a baby growing in its mother's womb is recording her emotions, and these emotions are affecting the baby's brain development. The period from pregnancy to age seven is critical for children, as they are downloading information from the environment into their brains.

It is worth repeating here that if both negative and false information are planted in our minds during our childhood, this has the potential to replicate itself during our adulthood in the form of negative thoughts, feelings, and behaviors. That belief is the cornerstone of a very successful worldwide United Way initiative, Success of Six. The philosophy of Success by Six is that, if the physical, emotional and social needs of children are met by the age of 6, they are more likely to enter school prepared to succeed academically and to go on to have successful careers. The concept of that initiative was an offshoot of the Jesuit ministry's belief, "Give me a child until he is seven, and I will give you a man." The principle is that the learning that occurs between birth and age seven will then go on to shape our behaviors in life. This belief is scientifically based. It is even used by advertising companies to manipulate children into consuming their products for life. For example, Dr. Matthew J. Edlund, MD, in his *Psychology Today* article titled "Give Us a Kid Till She's Seven and We'll Have Her for Life," did a fantastic job illustrating how certain food companies target children with alluring advertisements to hook them on junk food for a lifetime.

Whatever children hear from their parents, caregivers or other sources growing up will become part of their programming. For example, a child younger than seven may do something that a parent thought was foolish. The parent, without thinking, may yell at the kid and say, "That was stupid." Since the child's brain is unable to understand the difference between herself and the thing that she did, she could mentally download the message that, "I am stupid." Later on in life, she may find herself saying; "I am stupid" anytime she makes a mistake and may not have any recollection of how she came to be programmed that way. Basically, a lie was planted in this child's head that became her reality in life. In order to unearth these lies from childhood, we must first learn to identify them. This is why it is critical to be able to hear the feedback pertaining to us that are shared by others. We are not implying here that you need to believe or take what others say about you as the truth. You just need to be able to hear. It is irrelevant if their perceptions of you are accurate. It is more important for you to be able to gather information that may help you understand how you are presenting yourself to the world. We know this is not easy to do. Some people may need professional assistance to be able to accept that what their conscious mind picks up about them is just the tip of the iceberg. One way that we help people reprogram their brains is by developing and repeating mantras that are the opposite of whatever was mentally planted when they were children. As noted earlier, in the case of the child who was programmed to believe that she was stupid, she will need to correct this programming by repeating to herself, "I am smart."

Another example of this phenomenon is a child running around the house and coloring on the walls with markers. When the parent discovers what the child has done, his or her reaction may be to tell the child, "You've created a mess!" While the parent is understandably upset, what the child hears is, "I'm a mess!" The child then records this belief into their brain, and it has a lasting effect. The child may not remember the incident of coloring on the walls with markers, but he or she will remember, "I'm a mess," as this is what is recorded into the brain. The parent likely did not have malevolent intent, but the child still implanted this misinformation into his or her brain.

Lies from childhood can have such a lasting effect. When women come to counseling, it is important to look at their family history, including their early relationships with their parents, caregivers, and siblings. It is also important to assess how a woman views bonding and what her attachments were like growing up, whether it was a secure attachment in which she created strong connections with her caregivers, or if it was an insecure attachment due to trauma or neglect. Identifying these attachment styles can be especially useful for therapy, as research indicates that maladaptive attachments are linked to personality disorders and identity disturbances in adulthood (Beeney et al., 2017). Attachments can, therefore, be a part of our roots and have a strong influence on our internal programming as women.

Identifying and overcoming roots

If we need to overcome anything negative that was planted in us, we will need to start observing our feelings in various situations. This helps us identify what we have internalized from childhood that later in life make us feel or react in ways we did not intend or want. For instance, if you find yourself getting angry in certain situations, try to observe the circumstances to identify what has triggered that reaction. Perhaps you internalized from childhood that you were not deserving of respect, so when people disrespect you, this becomes triggering for you. Furthermore, because you feel that you are not worthy of respect, your programming will lead you to become attracted to circumstances that make you feel disrespected. You then become stuck in this system of functioning. In other words, the program continuously has been providing you with evidence to solidify your belief that this is your reality. Hence, you can hear yourself and others utter these words as their truth: "This is the way I am," or "Bad things always happened to me." These individuals may go on to provide you with plenty of evidence from their past. Unbeknownst to them, they have the power to stop these recurrences or habits. They can keep the limiting beliefs and the circumstances that they create in the rearview mirror by recognizing that they are a part of their program and by learning the appropriate actions to implement change. For example, one way to overcome the limiting belief that people always disrespect you is by repeating these mantras, "I respect myself. I am deserving of respect." This can redo your programming so that you don't continue to react to situations out of your control that you deem disrespectful. Your internal sense of respect will be so strong that you will have no need for external validation. That change alone can propel you to be more successful in the things you do in the future.

The process of changing can be challenging because the brain is hardwired to operate in a certain way. That is why it is important to repeat whatever mantra you have developed to overcome any false information that was planted during childhood.

After a while, this repetition develops new beliefs and thinking patterns by literally changing the way your brain is wired. It is especially helpful to repeat your mantra just before bedtime and first thing in the morning when the brain is operating in theta mode and is more receptive to changes. Theta brainwaves are also activated in deep meditation and visualization, which are the other two methods that we encourage our clients to practice when attempting to reprogram their brains.

Brainworks, a brain training company, describes theta brainwaves as follows: "Theta brain waves occur most often in sleep but are also dominant in deep meditation. Theta is our gateway to learning, memory, and intuition. In theta, our senses are withdrawn from the external world and focused on signals originating from within. It is that twilight state which we normally experience fleetingly as we wake or drift off to sleep. In theta, we are in a dream—vivid imagery, intuition, and information beyond our normal conscious awareness. It's where we hold our 'stuff,' our fears, troubled history, and nightmares" (Brainworks, n.d.).

You can think of this process as being similar to resetting a computer and reprogramming it. By making these changes to your brain, you are enabling it to produce new fruits, and these fruits are those that you'd want to produce. You can also view this as a way to end generational curses, and all the limiting beliefs that were passed down to us from generations via our culture and upbringing.

While making changes can help you to produce new fruits, you may encounter roadblocks along the way. One example we can offer from our counseling experiences is a very bright woman who was constantly comparing herself to others. She is an intellect, but it has been difficult for her to admit to herself that she is smart. Knowing her history, it was evident that traumatic events before the age of seven were at the root of her troubles. The first time she was challenged to repeat that she is as smart as other people, it was very painful for her to do. It was heart-wrenching to witness this brilliant woman struggling to repeat these words as tears dropped from her eyes. Her voice became very soft, almost like a whisper, and her throat was closing up as she was trying to hold back her tears. She had internalized this negative thought, that others are smarter and that she has to always struggle to be able to make it. That was her unconscious daily mantra for over 20 years. It was almost impossible for her to repeat these simple words: "I am smart." She had plenty of evidence that pointed to the truth, such as she was an A student in a challenging graduate program at a prestigious university. Her brain was spewing lies about who she was and they were being internalized and accepted as her truth. Again, because these beliefs were implanted in her brain at a time when she was creating her brain software (the subconscious mind) to help her navigate how to live in the world later, that simple exercise of repeating "I am smart" was very painful for her brain to perform. This exercise is the same as if you never went to the gym, went for the first time, and tried to lift a weight of 10 pounds or more. We are happy to report that after a few repetitions, she no longer has difficulties saying these words to herself. She is a healthier and happier person.

As this example demonstrates, it can be challenging to overcome negative roots on your own, which is why it is beneficial to see a therapist or a coach to begin the process of planting new seeds. You may feel comfortable reaching out to family for help, but family members, because they love you and want the best for you, are going to view the situation subjectively. Their viewpoint may be "foggy," and they may have difficulty providing accurate or effective solutions. This is why it may be helpful to seek help from a professional who can provide an objective viewpoint and assist you with working through the reprogramming of your internal dialogue. The ultimate goal of therapy and/or coaching is to alter any roots that have caused dysfunction. Fortunately, science shows that therapy can be highly effective for rewiring our brains. In fact, a review of numerous studies found that after individuals struggling with depression undergo therapy, including psychodynamic therapy, CBT, and behavioral therapy, they show differences in brain activity. This could be suggestive of improvements in emotional reactions (Sankar et al., 2018). This tells us that women can effectively change their programming, and thereby, their automatic behaviors, through therapy.

Why this is so important

As previously discussed, the roots that were planted during childhood can cause dysfunction in our lives because they become part of our subconscious mind, which automatically dictates our feelings and behaviors. Science says that 95 percent of how we go about our daily activities comes from the subconscious mind, and only five percent comes from our conscious mind. Hence the vital importance of ensuring that our subconscious mind has the information that we want to create the life that we desire. This will shield us from living our lives as victims of what was implanted in our minds as children. Our lack of awareness of this fact may cause us to move through life repeating the same mistakes, with no understanding of why we are finding ourselves in the same situations over and over again. Once you identify the subconscious thoughts that are driving your behaviors, you can change them so that you can begin to behave the way you would like to behave. We can't emphasize enough how critical it is to change the unwanted thoughts from our subconscious mind. Those thoughts may be what stand between you and your success in forming healthy relationships with yourself and others. They can be the stumbling blocks between you and your dream partner, career, and any success you seek in life.

For instance, some women who come to therapy may have issues with their mothers. Perhaps the mother was extremely critical or created issues surrounding their appearance or self-image. Once these women become adults, they may find that they are distrustful of others and worry that others are speaking critically of them, all because of the roots of the seeds that were planted during childhood. Over time, they may begin to believe that they are not good enough and begin to behave in ways that suggest they do not respect themselves. These behaviors could be driven by subconscious thoughts created during childhood. But by doing the work to identify and correct these thoughts, women can change their subconscious dialogue so that it is more beneficial for them.

Another problem that women may encounter is the subconscious belief that they must please others. They may grow up wanting to please their mothers or their grandmothers and feel as if they are never enough. For example, Oprah Winfrey has spoken about her own struggle with negative self-image. She shared that she realized that she needed to be physically, emotionally, and spiritually healthy for herself rather than care about being liked by others. Instead of losing weight to please others, she realized that she needed to be the healthiest version of herself (Medrano, 2017). Shifting our mindset from thinking we need to please others towards living for ourselves can help us to correct the subconscious thoughts that were planted during childhood.

Another reason that changing our subconscious thoughts is important is that when we internalize a belief about ourselves, we do not have to go out searching for validation from other people. For example, when a woman of color is asked, "Why do you think you're beautiful?" she may respond, "Because other people tell me I am." While it can certainly be uplifting to receive compliments from others, it is more valuable when we hold our own self-affirming beliefs, because these beliefs come from our core and do not rely on the opinions of other people.

This is of the utmost importance to the women who do not fit the image of beauty internalized from the predominant culture in the Western world. We are unique. There is no one like you in this world. So comparing yourself to others is like comparing apples to oranges. Accepting someone's truth instead of creating your own truth is likely to have unintended consequences on your health and happiness. The secret to being healthy and happy truly resides in the daily unconscious conversations we have with ourselves. So, making these unconscious conversations healthy and happy can transform our lives and help us accomplish things beyond our wildest dreams. Developing the ability to internalize positive thoughts about ourselves is perhaps one of the greatest gifts that women of color can derive from therapy or coaching. The African proverb "If there is no enemy inside, the enemy outside can do us no harm" illustrates the point we are making here. If we cultivate positive/healthy thoughts within our brains, negative/unhealthy factors, such as other people's hurtful words and behaviors cannot harm us.

It is especially important for women of color whose issues are rooted in their cultural history and family dynamics to work with a skilled, culturally competent therapist or coach for an accurate assessment of the internal conversations that have influenced their current feelings and behaviors. Therapeutic treatments or coaching may not be as effective if roots are not explored and addressed appropriately. For example, a study exploring depression treatment outcomes found that black women were less responsive to treatment when compared to white women (Cort et al., 2012). It is therefore critical that women of color work with therapists or coaches who are willing to explore their unique histories to evaluate how roots have produced current fruits, in order to ensure the best outcomes for them.

I, Edna, can think of an example from my own clinical experience with a client that demonstrates the importance of cultural competence when working to explore a client's roots. I recall my first job after graduation where I worked as a case manager as part of a team that included senior clinicians. As part of this team, our responsibilities included counseling individuals suffering from delusions to help improve their living situations.

For instance, one day I shared with my supervisor, a younger white female, how I was able to help a Haitian woman with understanding her symptoms of delusion and her acknowledging the importance of complying with her treatment plan in order for her to heal. I told my supervisor that I helped the client recall childhood memories of when she thought the moon was walking and running with her. Children in Haiti played this game often in my youth. Although, we saw and felt that the moon was following us, we knew that it was not real. Having been reminded of this scenario from her roots, the woman immediately understood and realized that the thoughts in her head were not real. She started taking her medication, began getting along better with her husband, and returned to her church community. After sharing with my supervisor my clinical progress with this client, she was dismissive and did not agree with my approach. Nonetheless, the positive outcome from the mental improvement of this patient was all the validation that I needed to affirm that cultural connection in therapeutic treatments does matter.

In summary, not only are your roots important, but it is also critical that you work with a counselor who is willing to recognize your culture and how it continues to contribute to your subconscious programming.

Strategies to try

Having learned about the importance of your roots, one strategy you can employ today is to assess a problem or negative belief you are experiencing and try to connect it to what you were taught as a child. Perhaps you feel that you are not capable of receiving a promotion at work. Explore the roots that may underlie this negative belief. Was there a time when you were not successful at something as a child, and someone was critical of your performance? Try to uncover the roots, and then create your positive mantra to override this negative root.

In order to change your thoughts, you can try the following exercise: Tonight, before you go to bed, reflect on three challenges you faced during the day. Replace those challenges with ways you would have liked the day to go. For example, if you had a conflict with your spouse, think about how you wish the conversation had gone, and what you could have said or done differently for things to turn out more favorably.

Reflections

Chapter 6

Training Your Brain

We have previously learned about the benefits of reprogramming the brain to overcome what we learned during childhood. There are also benefits to training the brain in general, so that we can become mentally and physically whole. The reason why training the brain is relevant is because achieving happiness and maintaining strong relationships requires that you be in alignment with your brain. We must train our brains in order to make the decisions that are best for us as women. When we train the brain, we are, in essence, caring for it.

The brain is an organ. So, it is also important to understand what brain type you have so that you can begin to understand why you behave the way that you do.

I, Edna, obtained a Brain Health certification from the Amen Clinic. The knowledge from my training allows me to incorporate results from a free online brain type assessment provided to the public by the Amen Clinic to better understand my therapy and coaching clients and to be more effective in developing goals that take into account brain health.

Here's the link to the free assessment, https://brainhealthassessment. com/assessment. Lastly, it can be helpful to think of the brain as a "garden." It can only produce plants from the seeds that were planted in it.

The brain as a garden

The brain is like a garden that needs to be weeded of unwanted thoughts and to be cared for on a daily basis in order to produce the fruits we desire. Everything we do is processed in the brain. If the brain is not healthy, we will not be emotionally or physically healthy either. The brain is divided into several lobes. The most important lobe associated with consciousness is the frontal lobe, which is the executive functioning center of the brain. We can think of this lobe as being like an executive in a business; it is in control. The brain allows us to make good decisions and refrain from engaging in things that can cause us harm. In other words, the frontal lobe is responsible for telling us, "You may do this, but there will be consequences." If this lobe is not healthy, you may find that your behavior is impulsive, and you are not able to control your actions. You may wish to do something, but you are unable to do it. In this way, the frontal lobe is vital in helping us differentiate between good and bad decisions.

There are other important lobes of the brain, such as the temporal lobe, which is especially relevant to functioning. This lobe plays a role in hearing as well as emotions. We can think of this part of the brain as digesting what is coming into the brain. It helps us to make interpretations about what we experience in life. With that being said, feelings of hurt and pain are processed in the temporal lobe. This lobe can be viewed as the place where we harvest the fruits of the plants that are planted there. As we begin to interpret the information that comes into the brain, it returns to us the recorded messages in the form of feelings that dictate our behaviors. In truth, we really hear more with our brain than with our ears because the brain interprets everything we hear. That is why it is very common for two people to hear the same lecture and come out with their own understanding of what they heard. We can begin to better regulate ourselves when we gain control over our emotional responses to what happens around us, and we can expect the temporal lobe to be involved in this process.

We want to emphasize here that it is beneficial to know that the brain is a control center that can become dysfunctional when it is not healthy. Just as the body can become unhealthy when it is overweight, the brain can become unhealthy when it is significantly stressed or overworked.

Reshaping the brain to experience gains

To have our brain garden produce the fruits that we want, we must correct unconscious, unhelpful programming, and fill it with helpful information. A therapist or a coach can assist with this process by listening to you speak, taking written and mental notes of what you have said, and then reflecting them back to you.

This process helps with connecting a client's history with their current emotional difficulties. For example, we may say, "You are having this problem now. Can you see how this is a repeated pattern from what you learned as a child?" A client can then discover what sort of unconscious programming from childhood has led to their current problems. As the client comes to the realization that unhelpful thoughts from childhood are leading the brain to be unhealthy, the client experiences a breakthrough. This will lead to actions that aim at changing limiting beliefs in order to eliminate the behaviors that cause them distress.

In addition to using positive affirmations and mantras as previously discussed, meditation is helpful for reshaping the brain. Meditation is really useful with bringing awareness of the unconscious thoughts that occur repeatedly throughout our day.

In 2005, the National Science Foundation published an article concerning human thoughts throughout the day. They discovered that the average person has about 12,000 to 60,000 thoughts per day. Of those, 80 percent are negative, and 95 percent are exactly the same repetitive thoughts as the day before (The Miracle Zone, 2012).

Through meditation, women can learn to let thoughts come in, and then let them go. This process trains the brain not to see negative thoughts as threats but as things that can come and go with no harm to the self. Some studies show that eight weeks of mindfulness meditation increased connections in the prefrontal cortex, which assists us in decreasing impulsive behaviors and responding more appropriately to stressful situations or thoughts. We often hear from clients that they distract themselves from their stressful thoughts by keeping busy. We usually ask them, where do you think these thoughts go when you are busy? They come to realize that it is just a temporary solution, as those thoughts always rush back with a vengeance when these people are idle. This is especially problematic for people who struggle with anxiety or trauma, as thoughts can be rather painful.

When meditating, people who live with anxiety and trauma may want to "run" instead of experiencing these painful thoughts. It is perfectly understandable that someone would rather avoid these thoughts than to sit in them. However, when one learns to treat these thoughts as just thoughts and not part of the present moment, then overtime these thoughts won't trigger the same emotional discomfort. Through this process, they can conquer the weeds in the garden of their brain and allow room for the seeds of their desired plants to grow freely and produce the fruits they desire.

Since meditation for people with a history of trauma can result in painful thoughts, it is helpful to work with a professional on guided meditation, instead of sitting alone with your thoughts. Meditation allows you to strengthen the muscles of the brain so that you learn you are safe, and painful thoughts do not actually mean you are in danger.

You can think of the analogy of going to the gym to train the muscles of the arm. Through a bicep curl, you curl the weight down, and then bring it back to your body. With meditation, you feel your painful thoughts, and then bring yourself back to the present. Throughout this process, you stay still, engage in deep breathing, and train the brain to identify the thoughts that are making you uncomfortable. Next you would let go of these thoughts rather than holding onto them. This exercise strengthens the muscles of your brain that communicate to the body that you are currently safe rather than being in danger from past traumatic events. One study that found this practice to be effective involved women who were victims of domestic violence. They engaged in a weekly mindfulness session for eight weeks. Each session involved guided meditation, gentle movement exercises, and a group discussion. After the intervention, they demonstrated decreases in depression and trauma as well as improvements in attachment (Kelly & Garland, 2016).

Transforming the mind through good nutrition

In addition to psychological practices like meditation and positive affirmations, women can improve brain functioning by improving their physical health. One strategy for achieving this is through proper nutrition. When you eat, at least 20 percent of the energy from your food goes to nourish your brain. Fernando Gomez-Pinilla, a professor in the Departments of Neurosurgery and Integrative Biology and Physiology at UCLA Medical School, stated, "The brain is an energy-hungry organ. Despite comprising only two percent of the body's weight, the brain gobbles up more than 20 percent of daily energy intake. Because the brain demands such high amounts of energy, the foods we consume greatly affect brain function, including everything from learning and memory to emotions."

In addition, studies suggest the quality of the foods consumed over our lifetime affects the structure and function of the brain (BrainFacts.org, 2012). This means that if you are not eating properly, your brain is not going to be able to help you function optimally. It is essential to give your brain the nutrition that it needs.

Women can certainly improve brain functioning by giving it proper nutrition, but the best diet varies for each individual woman. Some people may require a higher protein intake to train the brain, whereas others may require more complex carbohydrates. As noted earlier, the brain is an organ. Hence, it is dependent on proper nutrition to fully function. If the brain is filled with unhealthy items such as processed sugars and simple carbohydrates, like breads and potatoes, we are at risk of developing diabetes, which certainly affects the brain. In addition, a poor diet on its own, without concurrent health issues, can negatively affect the brain, leading to impulsivity and mood fluctuations. It is for this reason that when people begin reducing unhealthy items in their diets, they begin to see an improvement in their mood. There is a direct relationship between what we eat and how we feel and function.

To understand this relationship even further, we must think of the brain as a control center. Whatever we eat is fuel for the brain, and we must eat what is necessary to give the brain ongoing fuel for functioning. This can be difficult for some women because of cultural diets. Some cultures consume large quantities of white rice or pasta, which creates an instant surge of energy (high blood sugar level) in the brain, followed by a crash in which energy is depleted (low blood sugar level).

Did you know that low blood sugar might cause you to be irritable or angry? This does not allow the brain to function optimally over time. Think of your body as being a luxury model car; you would not fill this type of car with cheap gasoline. Instead, you would care for it with premium fuel. Our bodies are the same way; we should treat them with tender care. Therefore, we should not expect our bodies to function at their best if we are not providing them with the appropriate fuel.

To achieve optimal brain functioning, we must find a diet that provides balance and meets our unique needs. This typically involves following a diet that is rich in healthy proteins and contains an appropriate amount of complex carbohydrates, mostly in the form of fruits and vegetables. The most important component of a healthy diet is finding something that works for you and making it a lifestyle. You must also keep in mind that the diet that works for you may be different from what works for someone else. It can be helpful to look at the healthy components of the diets that are popular in your culture, and incorporate these components into your lifestyle.

Your biology may also affect what foods are healthiest for you. For instance, there is some evidence that individuals of African and Asian descent may be more likely to be allergic to dairy, whereas this allergy is less prevalent in those of European descent.

One way to determine if the food you are eating is helpful for your biology is to complete a blood test, which will tell you what foods you should avoid. The test is called a food inflammation test (FIT), and it will uncover any food sensitivities you may have. You can check with a wellness practitioner to test you, or you can order a kit to complete at home and determine how foods affect you.

As a woman of color, you may be especially at risk of food sensitivities. In fact, a study in the *Journal of Allergy and Clinical Immunology* found that food allergies are more common among non-Hispanic blacks (Lui et al., 2010). This means that dietary advice presented to the mainstream culture may not be suitable for you. For example, the benefits of consuming dairy products are sometimes touted in the media, but as mentioned above, people of color may be more likely to be sensitive to dairy. You may need to do some exploration with a culturally sensitive medical professional to determine the best diet for you. Knowing what foods to avoid and which to include in your diet can help you to fuel your brain so it can function at its best.

Beauty sleep for the brain

Beyond providing the brain with proper fuel for optimal health, it is critical to prioritize sleep. Some women may put pressure on themselves to stay up long after their children have gone to bed in order to complete household tasks. Additionally, professional women that are either single or married may feel the need to continue working late into the evening in order to propel their careers forward. Ultimately, this can do more harm than good to the brain.

Did you know that the only way for the brain to cleanse itself is through deep and REM sleep? All organs have a way to cleanse themselves, and if anything is obstructing the pathway, the body deteriorates. In other words, this obstruction can cause somewhat of a poison to the body, which can lead to death.

Lack of restful sleep harms our brains and causes serious mental health impairments in the long run. You can deprive your brain of quality sleep for only so long before you begin to notice the negative effects on your brain. Just like the liver, you can feed it alcohol for a long time until you develop cirrhosis of the liver.

Gadie et al., (2017) found that better sleep was linked to improved mental health, as well as better cognitive performance. They also found that sleeping too much or too little was associated with a greater risk of depression and anxiety. Research also shows that REM sleep is particularly important for mental health, as it plays a role in consolidating emotional memories (Nishida et al., 2009). These findings indicate that healthy sleep habits can truly transform the mind.

Achieving emotional gains

Another form of healthy training to the brain involves restoring it emotionally. Similiar to feeding the brain healthy foods, we must also nourish it with positive thoughts. When you have achieved emotional gains, you are no longer reactive to things that once could have made you angry. Instead, you maintain a sense of calmness.

For example, if you are emotionally restored as a woman of color, if a Caucasian person insults your race, instead of becoming angry, you remain calm. The reason for this is that an emotionally trained brain understands that a person who insults you is not talking to you; that person is talking to himself or herself. Remember, the enemy outside can do no harm if there is no enemy inside. If you respect yourself, then disrespect from others will not affect you emotionally. Arriving at this level of emotional gain is one of the most challenging but powerful goals of retraining the brain.

Let's further clarify this point. For example, imagine someone referring to you as "stupid." You know that this person doesn't know how accomplished and intelligent you are. So, this insult should not affect you. If you are secure in your accomplishments, you likely would not give a second thought to what the person said and would move on to continue your work with no emotional pain. On the other hand, if you allow yourself to be offended, you may react negatively and appear somewhat "stupid," thereby confirming what the person originally said about you. This is why it is so important to respect yourself and know your value so that negative comments from others do not negatively impact your emotions.

This example seems especially relevant for women of color because, for us, racism is perpetuated in the same way. Victims of racism are seen as victims, causing them to behave as such. They maintain this sense of victimization and continue the legacy of slavery. However, the day we proclaim our power as women and refute the ideology that we are victims will be the day we overcome this legacy. To recognize that we are capable and deserving beings is the best thing that we can do for ourselves as women of color. Through the retraining of our brains, we can begin to see ourselves as capable instead of victims of the legacy of slavery.

The impact of trauma, both physical and emotional

You may also have to work toward making emotional gains if you have experienced some sort of trauma during your lifetime, including a physical trauma, such as a traumatic brain injury. Fortunately for us, given the proper nutrition and time, the brain can heal itself from injuries.

I can take myself (Regina) as an example. When I was very young, I was involved in a serious car accident, during which I sustained a significant traumatic brain injury (TBI) with loss of consciousness (LOC). In fact, my family was unsure if I would survive at the time. As a result of the head injury, I had cognitive difficulties that I needed to overcome. We know that the brain is a complex organ that functions through interconnections. The advantage that I had is that I was young. As I recovered, I went through vicarious functioning, which is when other parts of the brain tries to compensate for the reduced ability by working harder. Take for example, someone who is blind. It is not uncommon for the sense of hearing or sense of touch to increase in an effort to compensate for the loss of vision. Because I was young, my brain was able to heal quicker, and it was able to create new connections between the different networks. This is referred to as plasticity. The research shows that the brain has the capacity to heal, make the necessary changes and improvements to give someone the best possible chance to function. This does not mean that my journey was an easy walk. I had to relearn a variety of things that I previously performed with ease. Even as an adult, I have learned to use cognitive strategies to maximize my compensatory skills. Some challenges that are common after a brain injury is the tendency to get cognitively and emotionally drained. The average person that has to deal with a lot of stress and who is not careful can easily exhaust their cognitive resources. After a TBI, that cognitive resource is even more limited. This means that I had to learn ways to accommodate by refraining from going into or engaging in activities that I knew would or could easily lead to cognitive or emotional exhaustion. Through my journey, I discovered and introduced techniques that have helped me stay in the present, remain grounded, and maximize my mental capacity. The funny thing is that we often take many of these simple things for granted. For example, taking a break before you reach a certain level of fatigue can give your body a chance to rejuvenate and prevent your organs from overworking themselves. Breathing, especially deep breathing exercises are essential given that the brain requires at least 20% of the oxygen we take in every day. Prioritizing sleep and nutrition in the context of reorganizing the day/night cycle (circadian rhythm) can go very far in ensuring that you do not have to allocate mental resources to things that can be routine. I can say that the process of putting compensatory actions into place has aided me physically, cognitively, emotionally, and adaptively. In fact, these are some of the things that helped me heal and grow enough to later pursue a higher education. So, I am a testimony that these techniques can work.

Emotional trauma that is endured during childhood can also alter the brains response to stress. We can use childhood sexual abuse as an example. Children who are sexually abused at times suffer from feelings of shame and guilt because they were sexually aroused during the abuse. They may misinterpret these sensations as pleasurable and create a false narrative of themselves as being flawed due to the sexual enjoyment received from the abuse. This can cause them to keep the assault a secret and hinder their potential to truly heal from the trauma. It is important for victims of trauma to reframe the experience, so they are not blaming themselves and creating a pattern of negative self-thoughts in the brain.

To overcome trauma, it is also crucial to understand the autonomic nervous system, which includes both the sympathetic and the parasympathetic nervous systems. It is called autonomic because it is automatic, and we have no power over it. The sympathetic nervous system is associated with the "fight or flight" survival response, whereas the parasympathetic nervous system is responsible for functions such as regulating digestion and reducing the heart rate and blood pressure. With that being said, the parasympathetic nervous system doesn't only deal with calming us down; there is a more primitive side of it that makes us freeze. Dr. Seth Porges referred to this "freeze" process as the "red zone" (Porges, 2011).

The red zone is very crucial in understanding and overcoming trauma or chronic stress. Our sympathetic nervous system goes into action automatically when we are exposed to stress. It sends the signal to fight or take flight/escape. However, when we have no option to do either of these things, the parasympathetic mode of freezing comes into play. It is very important to understand this phenomenon that Dr. Stephen Porges explained so eloquently in the polyvagal theory when dealing with your own trauma and in working with people affected by trauma. The way it is illustrated in the wild is when the lion has caught his prey. When the animal is put in a position where it feels powerless, its body goes limp. This is the same symptom we refer to in victims of trauma when we say they have dissociated. Sometimes we refer to them as having an out-of-body experience.

The reason this is relevant is because many trauma victims were put in a situation where they felt powerless to escape. Many blamed themselves for not fighting, and worst of all, others may make re-traumatizing comments afterward pertaining to what they would have done or what the victim could have done differently.

That is one of the reasons we mentioned how important it is to understand the freezing mechanism of the autonomic nervous system. This is a system that is totally out of our control. When faced with or dealing with trauma, this system automatically does its job, and we are at its mercy. Nature doesn't make mistakes, but as humans, we have an advantage over other animals. We hold the ability to train or retrain our brain to allow the autonomic nervous system to make different choices or decisions that are in our best interest. Rewiring the brain is about using the science of neuroplasticity to create different thoughts that help us to feel differently and produce different behaviors.

You will know that you have successfully rewired your brain, to respond at your command during moments of distress rather than fire automatically, when you realize the lack of emotional power emotions such as anger and anxiety have on the self. Yes, these emotions can adversely affect us if we allow it, but if we adjust our thinking and take control of these emotions then our responses to incidents that use to trigger them will also shift. An example I, Edna, can offer is when something offensive happened to me, and I found myself reacting more calmly than I would have in the past. I was even surprised at how wisely I handled the situation. People who witnessed the event came to me to express their sympathy. I reflected on the incident later to understand what happened so that I could identify what was different, in order to replicate the same result in the future. I remembered that when the event happened, I felt like my ego took a blow, and I wanted to flee. Then, I understood it was my brain reacting automatically to save me from the perceived embarrassment. However, because I already did the work of knowing my value, the relaxation response of my parasympathetic nervous system got activated automatically. So, my brain quickly stopped to see the offensive action as a danger and I was able to overcome it. I also recalled that when those that witnessed the incident came to talk to me, my responses focused on externalizing the event rather than internalizing it. I knew that it was not about me, so I didn't take responsibility for the actions of the person who committed the offensive act. Had I taken responsibility for the other person's action, I would have gone inside my mind to criticize myself for doing something wrong that warranted that person's behavior.

You see, we often take responsibility for people's actions and reactions because of our own brain wiring. We hope this example illustrates how important it is to retrain our brains to have the reactions that we want instead of being at the mercy of our past programming.

One way to conceptualize retraining the brain to overcome automatic or trauma-related responses is to think of the brain as a highway. There are many potential pathways or highways in the brain. Over time, with trauma, a specific pathway becomes the one most traveled and is, therefore, the highway that we automatically take when we are presented with a threat or a stressful situation. When triggered, we automatically travel down this pathway with a trauma response, such as lashing out or shutting down emotionally to protect ourselves.

Fortunately, we can make other, healthier highways our new norm due to the neuroplasticity of the brain. This concept says that we can reshape our brains and thereby change our behaviors. We can achieve this change by trying something new, such as learning a new skill or consciously choosing a different reaction. For instance, we can learn to identify what our trauma is, what situations trigger it, and how we typically react. We can then make a conscious effort to choose a new, healthier reaction to replace the previous reaction. Over time, with repetition, we can develop a new highway, so that the healthier reaction becomes our default response (Healing Trauma Center, 2020). By strengthening new highways within the brain, we are retraining it so that we can be more in control of our emotions and reactions in order to live the life we have always desired. While this process is certainly achievable, it can be difficult to undergo on your own. This is where a trained therapist becomes a valuable resource for you.

Whether you are recovering from a brain injury or simply wishing to achieve better regulation of your emotions, it is important to remember that the process begins within you. Your brain is an organ that controls your thoughts and behaviors, and over time, what we do repeatedly becomes our life. This process is subconscious, but by retraining our brains with repetition, meditation, proper sleep and nutrition, we can reprogram our brains so that our desired thoughts and actions become automatic.

Something to try this week

Have you ever eaten a large meal, or indulged in a sugary dessert, and found that you felt "foggy" afterward? Chances are that you were not fueling your brain properly, or perhaps you consumed food to which your body had an allergy or sensitivity. To begin to explore food sensitivities that may be harming your brain function, keep a food diary for a week. Write down everything you eat in a given day, and make a note of how you feel after each meal, and at the end of each day. Look for patterns. Do you notice that you always feel sluggish after consuming cheese? Perhaps you find that you feel better when consuming protein-rich foods. Use what you learn from your food diary to create a healthy, nourishing diet that fuels your brain for optimal functioning. This process should not take the place of nutritional advice from a medical professional, but it may be the first step toward determining which foods nourish you best.

Chapter 7

Thrive in Your Tribe

In addition to training your brain and learning how to be the best version of yourself, it is important to find a tribe of people who support you. Sometimes you may feel alone, but when you build a community of trust, you have natural support. In order to survive and thrive in this world as women of color, we need to have a community of individuals who support us. When you're going through trying times and are feeling depressed, individuals in your community can provide you with a different outlook. If you have been struggling mentally and emotionally, you may develop learned helplessness, in which you feel you cannot be successful. Within your community of trust, you can see people struggling but still achieving, and this can reverse feelings of learned helplessness.

Your community of trust becomes a source of energy for you when you don't have it. In those moments when you feel so depressed that you simply cannot do anything, members of your community can lend a helping hand. Your community of trust should comprise of people who will genuinely be present to help you with your struggles when you lack motivation or feel hopeless.

What does a community of trust look like?

Perhaps the most important fact about a community of trust is that there is no specific formula for what constitutes a community of trust for each person. The community of trust is made up of individuals with whom you bond the most. Some people naturally create stronger bonds with older individuals, so it should never be assumed that your community should be made up of only people your own age.

It could be argued that the best community of trust is comprised of different individuals. For instance, your community of trust can be made up of elders who provide you with the wisdom of life experience, as well as knowledge that is sincere. These individuals can keep you grounded as they talk about historical struggles, such as how they thrived despite racial biases. On the other hand, it is helpful to have the perspective of people your own age, who can provide a different lens through which to view your life situation.

It is important to bring people into your circle of trust that will be able to provide the support that you need. If, as a woman of color, you do not have people in your immediate family who are able to provide wisdom or support, you can seek models of older individuals or historical figures who exemplify what you would like to achieve. These may be people, such as Madam C.J. Walker, whom you can read about in books. She serves as a role model for black women, as she was the first woman of color to become a millionaire in the United States. As the daughter of a slave, she earned her fortune creating homemade hair products for women of color (History, 2020). Your community can certainly include famous figures, like Madam C.J. Walker, who can bring energy into your life by reminding you of what women are capable of achieving.

Like other aspects of mental well being, the community of trust must begin with us. This means that we must have trust in ourselves and love for ourselves before we can invite people into our community of trust. This is because you will attract who you are; if you want to live a happy and healthy life, you first need to accept this fact. If you are struggling with building a community of trust and find that you are in relationships with others who are abusive or dishonest, you must ask yourself, "What is it about me that makes me okay with being in these relationships?"

How do you build a community of trust?

Building your community of trust requires you to be vulnerable and tell others what it is that you need or want. If you are always the one who is going out and helping others, but you never give others a chance to help you, this may be an indication that you do not trust people and are not comfortable being vulnerable. Creating your community, therefore, may require you to turn inward and uncover what about you is holding you back from creating such a community.

By working on yourself, you will be better equipped to attract people with whom you can truly connect. As social creatures, we seek connections with others, so it makes sense that forming such a community with other trusting women would be nurturing to the self. One sign that you have found your community of trust is when you have a group of women you can go to and "let your hair down." These are women with whom you can laugh and be genuine, which is important because humor is healing. We need these types of women within our community of trust, and they should be women we can turn to at any time for support. For instance, a member of your community may drive hours to visit when she knows that you are struggling with depression and need her to lend a listening ear.

Mental health professionals as members of the circle of trust

While having a community of friends is essential, sometimes women may find it necessary to seek counseling from a mental health professional or a coach in order to expand their community of trust. Our primary goal in working with women of color is to teach them that everything begins and ends with them. You cannot control what others do; you can only control your actions and your reactions to others. This is an important lesson to learn. When you master this concept, you can truly live a happier and healthier version of yourself. If you are unhappy with those that you consider to be members of your community of trust, a mental health professional or a coach can help you to uncover what it is within you that is leading to this dissatisfaction.

Deciding whether to seek outside help can be difficult, and women may prefer to seek the assistance of family members or friends instead of inviting a professional into their circle of trust. Unfortunately, this can, at times, be counterproductive. As discussed earlier, our loved ones have a subjective opinion of our lives, and they tend to project their own viewpoints onto our situations. They will give their own opinions and tell us what we need to do, but a professional will give a different lens that is primarily objective. In counseling or coaching, a professional joins with women in the process of exploring themselves and becoming the best versions of themselves. In this way, the professional becomes a part of the circle of trust temporarily, until the client is able to address and learn coping skills to resolve problems from their past and focus on the present.

If your emotional issues require you to see a mental health professional, the benefit is that they have undergone training that makes them much less subjective. These professionals are trained to be more aware of their own viewpoints and baggage, and gain the skill set that allows them to be objective without projecting their perspectives onto their clients. Whereas, loved ones have a tendency to be more subjective because their primary motivation may be to protect us from harm. They become fearful when they hear that a loved one is struggling, and their body enters the "fight or flight" mode, so they aim to fix the problem.

On the other hand, professionals like counselors and coaches are not fixers. They are trained to refrain from projecting their own viewpoints and biases onto clients. Instead, professionals explore issues with clients, and the client ultimately decides what is best. Because professionals are not merely fixers, they can become an instrumental part of the community of trust when friends and family are unhelpful because of their subjectivity.

Conclusions

As you build your community of trust, whether this involves a mental health professional or not, it is critical to remember that despite our experience and wisdom, there is always more that we can learn. For example, a senior counselor may feel ashamed to seek out the advice of a junior counselor, but the younger professional can have helpful wisdom to impart. No matter your stage in life, you need people you can turn to, even if you are experienced and successful yourself.

Lastly, you need to remember that you must first work on self-love before you can lead a truly fulfilling life. You are the foundation of your life, and if there are cracks within your foundation, you'll be unable to build the house you desire. If you are struggling with cracks within yourself or find that you are having difficulty finding balance and building a supportive community, it may be time to reach out for professional intervention.

To end, we want to reiterate that there may be a stigma surrounding therapy and psychological services, with some women of color believing that asking for help is a sign of weakness. On the contrary, reaching out for help indicates that you are strong enough to seek self-improvement so that you can become the best version of yourself. We are excited to go on this journey with you. We believe that the best for you is yet to come!

References

Adkins-Jackson, P.B., Turner-Musa, J., & Chester, C. (2019). The path to better health for black women: Predicting self-care and exploring its mediation role on stress and health. *Inquiry, 56*, 1-8. https://doi.org/10.1177/0046958019870968

American Psychiatric Association. (2013). *Diagnostic and Statistical Manual of Mental Disorders* (5th ed.). American Psychiatric Association. American Psychological Association. (n.d.). *Different approaches to psychotherapy.* https://www.apa.org/topics/therapy/psychotherapy-approaches

Arreola, C. (2015). *8 facts about Latinos & mental health you need to know.* Retrieved from https://www.huffpost.com/entry/8-facts-about-latinos-men_b_8306396

Baker, K. G. (2015). *Bowen family systems couple coaching.* In A. S. Gurman, J. L. Lebow, & D. K. Snyder (Eds.), *Clinical handbook of couple therapy* (p. 246–267). The Guilford Press.

Baratta, M. (2018). *Self-care 101.* Retrieved from https://www.psychologytoday.com/us/blog/skinny-revisited/201805/self-care-101

Beeney, J.E., Wright, A.G.C., Stepp, S.D., Hallquist, M.N., Lazarus, S.A., Beeney, J.R.S., & Scott, L.N. (2017). Disorganized attachment and personality functioning in adults: A latent class analysis. *Personality Disorders: Theory, Research, and Treatment, 8*(3), 206-216.

Beer, J.E., & Stief, E. (1997). *The mediator's handbook*. New Society Publishers.

BrainFacts.org. (2012). *How does the brain use food as energy?* Retrieved from https://www.brainfacts.org/ask-an-expert/how-does-the-brain-use-food-as-energy

Brain Works. (n.d.). *What are brain waves?* Retrieved from https://brainworksneurotherapy.com/what-are-brainwaves

Chapman, G. (2015). *The 5 love languages*. Northfield Publishing.

Chevigny, K, Ness, M., & Cioffi, L. (Producers), Hallgren, N. (Director). (2020). Becoming [Documentary]. United States:Netflix.

Cort, N.A., Gamble, S.A., Chaudron, L.H., Lu, N., He, H., & Talbot, N.L. (2012). Predictors of treatment outcomes among depressed women with childhood sexual abuse histories. *Depression & Anxiety, 29*(6), 479-486. https://doi.org/10.1002/da.21942

Cuijpers, P. (2017). Psychotherapies vs. pharmacotherapies vs. combination therapies in depressive and anxiety disorders. *European Psychiatry, 41*, S6. https://doi.org/10.1016/j. eurpsy.2017.01.007

Cuijpers, P., Donker, T., Weissman, M.M., Ravitz, P., & Crista, I.A. (2016). Interpersonal psychotherapy for mental health problems: A comprehensive meta-analysis. *The American Journal of Psychiatry, 173*(7), 680-687. https://doi.org/10.1176/appi.ajp.2015.15091141

Elavsky. (2010). Longitudinal examination of the exercise and self-esteem model in middle-aged women. *Journal of Sport and Exercise Psychology, 32*(6), 862-880. https://doi.org/10.1123/jsep.32.6.862

Gadie, A. Shafto, M., Yue Leng, C., & Kievet, R.A. (2017). How are age-related differences in sleep quality associated with health outcomes? An epidemiological investigation in a UK cohort of 2406 adults. *BMJ Open, 7,* e014920. https://doi.org/10.1136/bmjopen-2016-014920

Gottman, J. & Silver, N. (2012). *What makes Love Last?:How to build love and avoid Betrayal.* New York, NY: Simon & Schuster Paperbacks.

Grant, J. (2019). *We applaud these Black celebs for helping to erase mental health stigmas with their testimonies.* Retrieved from https://www.essence.com/lifestyle/health-wellness/black-celebs-help-erase-mental-health-stigmas-encourage-therapy/

Gregory, V.L. (2019). Cognitive-behavioral therapy for anxious symptoms in persons of African descent: A meta-analysis. *Journal of Social Service Research, 45*(1), 87-101. https://doi.org/10.1080/01488376.2018.1479344

Guntrip, H.Y. (2018). *Personality structure and human interactions: The developing synthesis of psychodynamic theory.* Routledge.

Hales, A.H., Wesselman, E.D., & Williams, K.D. (2016). Prayer, self-affirmation, and distraction improve recovery from short-term ostracism. *Journal of Experimental Social Psychology, 64,* 8-20. https://doi.org/10.1016/j.jesp.2016.01.002

Healing Trauma Center. (2020). Neuroplasticity and rewiring the brain. Retrieved from https://healingtraumacenter.com/neuroplasticity-and-rewiring-the-brain/

History. (2020). *Madam C.J. Walker.* Retrieved from https://www.history.com/topics/black-history/madame-c-j-walker

Jakowska, M., Brown, J., Ronaldson, A., & Steptoe, A. (2015). The impact of a brief gratitude intervention on subjective well-being, biology, and sleep. *Journal of Health Psychology, 21*(10), 2207-2217. https://doi.org/10.1177/1359105315572455

Kelly, A., & Garland, E.L. (2016). Trauma-informed mindfulness-based stress reduction for female survivors of interpersonal violence: Results from a stage 1 RCT. *Journal of Clinical Psychology, 72*(4), 311-328. https://doi.org/10.1002/jclp.22273

Liu, A.H., Jaramillo, R., Sicherer, S.H., Wood, R.A., Bock, S.A., Burks, W., Massing, M., Cohm R.D., & Zeldin, D.C. (2010). National prevalence and risk factors for food allergy and relationship to asthma: Results from the National Health and Nutrition Examination Survey 2005-2006. *Journal of Allergy and Clinical Immunology, 126*(4), 798-806. https://doi.org/10.1016/j.jaci.2010.07.026

Marselle, M.R., Irvine, K.N., & Warber, S.L. (2013). Walking for well-being: Are group walks in certain types of natural environments better for well-being than group walks in urban environments? *International Journal of Environmental Research and Public Health, 10*(11), 5603-5628. https://doi.org/10.3390/ijerph10115603

Medrano, K. (2017). *Oprah Winfrey doesn't care how much she weighs.* Retrieved from https://www.essence.com/celebrity/oprah-weight-watchers-42-pounds/

National Alliance on Mental Illness. (2020). *Psychosocial treatments.* Retrieved from https://nami.org/About-Mental-Illness/Treatments/Psychosocial-Treatments

Neal-Barnett, A. (n.d.). *To be female, anxious and Black.* Retrieved from https://adaa.org/learn-from-us/from-the-experts/blog-posts/consumer/be-female-anxious-and-black

Nishida, M., Pearsall, J., Buckner, R.L., & Walker, M.P. (2009). REM sleep, prefrontal theta, and the consolidation of human emotional memory. Cerebral Cortex, 19(5), 1158-1166. https://doi.org/10.1093/cercor/bhn155

Pollack, M.H., Jensen, J.E., Simon, N.M., Kaufman, R.E., & Renshaw, P.F. (2008). High-field MRS study of GABA, glutamate and glutamine in social anxiety disorder: Response to treatment with levetiracetam. *Progress in Neuro-Psychopharmacology and Biological Psychiatry, 32*(3), 739-743. https://doi.org/10.1016/j.pnpbp.2007.11.023

Porges, S.W. (2011). *The Polyvagal Theory: Neurophysiological foundations of emotions, attachment, communication, and self-regulation.* W.W. Norton & Company.

Sankar, A., Melin, A., Lorenzetti, V., Horton, P., Costafrada, S.G., & Fu, C.H.Y. (2018). A systematic review and meta-analysis of the neural correlates of psychological therapies in major depression: *Psychiatry Research, 279,* 31-39. https://doi.org/10.1016/j.pscychresns.2018.07.002

The Miracle Zone. (2012). *80% of thoughts are negative... 95% are repetitive.* Retrieved from https://faithhopeandpsychology.wordpress.com/2012/03/02/80-of-thoughts-are-negative-95-are-repetitive/Queensland Brain Institute. (2017). *What are neurotransmitters?* Retrieved from https://qbi.uq.edu.au/brain/brain-physiology/what-are-neurotransmitters

Virgili, M. (2015). Mindfulness-based interventions reduce psychological distress in working adults: A meta-analysis of intervention studies. *Mindfulness, 6,* 326-337. https://doi.org/10.1007/s12671-013-0264-0 https://www.brainhealthassessment.com/assessment

**This book was published with the support of
The Bestsellers Academy.**

Do you have a book on the inside of you?
Let us get your story out of your belly and into an international
bestselling book!
Phone: 1-868-374-7441
Email: success@thebestsellersacademy.com
Website: TheBestsellersAcademy.com